The Chemical Elements

The fascinating story of their discovery and of the famous scientists who discovered them

Nechaev & Jenkins

With illustrations by
Borin Van Loon

Tarquin Publications

This wonderful account of the discovery of the chemical elements first
came to my attention at the end of 1994. It came in the form of a small
red book, printed on war-time paper and looking rather faded. It had
been published in 1944. It conveys in a remarkable way the excitement and tribulations of scientific discovery and I immediately decided
to republish it.

At the same time, I have taken the opportunity to add a new chapter
which brings the story up to date. This explains how nuclear science
and quantum mechanics have added so much to our understanding of
what the chemical elements are and how they are related. At the same
time it brings a clear explanation of the patterns in the periodic table,
patterns and similarities which were so puzzling to Mendeleev and the
scientists of his time.

All attempts to trace the author have failed, but the publishers would be
truly delighted to have news of him or his family. It is most satisfying
that his work lives on and can now serve to inspire another generation.

Gerald Jenkins, Stradbroke, Spring 1997.

I. Nechaev

In April 2003, five years after the publication of
this book in 1997, a copy found its way to
Professor Victor Pan in New York and the mystery
of the whereabouts of 'I. Nechaev' was solved.
It was the pen-name of Professor Pan's father
which he used for the book when it was written
and published in Moscow in 1939.

The story of the author, told in the form of a letter
from his son to the publisher, is given on page 4.

© 2003:   I. Nechaev, G.W.Jenkins
© 1997:   First Edition
I.S.B.N.:   1 899618 11 2
Illustrations: Borin Van Loon
Design: Magdalen Bear
Printing: Burlington Press, Cambridge   All rights reserved

Tarquin Publications
Stradbroke
Diss
Norfolk IP21 5JP
England

CONTENTS

Dear Mr Jenkins,

The discovery of your book 'The Chemical Elements' written by my father has been such a delightful surprise for me. The Russian edition was republished in the USSR in 1960 but I thought until now that the English edition had not been reprinted since the forties.

I am very pleased to be able to tell you something about my father.

His name was Yakov (that is Jacob) Solomonovich Pan and he was born in 1906, in Berdichev (Ukraine), then a small Jewish 'shtettle'. He came from a poor family, and his father had 18 children of whom just 10 survived childhood. His mother had died while he was young and there was never enough money to educate the children. Boots were a difficulty too and because he shared a single pair with his brother, they could only go to school in turn. In spite of reading everything of the very little that was available in an attempt to educate himself, he felt terribly isolated in such a remote place. However, in 1921, he sent a letter to the Minister of Education, A. Lunacharsky, and a miracle happened. Lunacharsky was so impressed that he decided to help and in December of the same year my father was offered a place at a school in Moscow. His ability to study by himself was encouraged and he then had much more access to books and libraries. He won a place at MVTU, one of the best Technical Universities in Moscow and studied chemistry. He also became very excited about scientific discoveries and the people who had made them. Finally he began to write about them and his first book, 'Chemical Elements' was published in 1939. It was an immediate success and every newspaper in Moscow devoted a large article to it. It was reprinted many times in Russian and was translated into English and published in the USA in 1942 by Coward-McCann. I was also interested to hear that the British edition that was given to you was published in 1944 by Lindsay Drummond. During this later period in Moscow my father was suffering from tuberculosis and so did not have to join the army. However, as the Germans approached Moscow, he volunteered and unfortunately was killed in 1941 near Lake Seliger (about 220 miles west-north-west of Moscow). He was 35.

I was born in 1939 and have no brothers and sisters. I only know of my father from what my mother told me, from their diaries and from the words of our friends and relatives, all of whom have passed away, except for my cousin Vladimir Pan, an internationally known physicist in Kiev. He told me that he chose to follow a scientific career after being inspired by reading 'Chemical Elements' as a child. I married Lydia Perelman in Moscow in 1972 and we emigrated to the USA in 1976. In my childhood and my youth I had greatly admired my father's books, as did many of my friends. I therefore find myself rather surprised, very happy and very grateful to you to learn that my father's work continues to arouse interest more than 60 years after its completion. As far as I know, the pen-name I. Nechaev was only chosen after a lot of thought. Following the success of 'Chemical Elements', he then used it for his other books, 'The White Dwarf' and 'Chemical Weapon'. The name 'Pan' was not a good one for an author to use at that time in Russia because it was associated with the land-owning classes in the Ukraine and Poland. This use of a pen-name also helps to explain why you were not able to find the name anywhere and makes it even more remarkable that a copy should ever find its way to me, Victor Pan. The book was discovered by one of my Ph.D. students, Taj-Eddin, just a few days ago. He was studying computer science but also became very interested in reading about the history of science. I told him about my father's 1942 edition of 'Chemical Elements'. He searched for it and amazingly found a copy of your 1997 edition in the library! How astonishing!

I am delighted that a new edition is to be published and that the memory of my father and his work lives on. I also enclose a copy of an old photograph that my mother had kept and passed on to me.

With my best regards,

Victor Pan

Distinguished Professor
Math. and Computer Science Dept.
Lehman College, CUNY
Bronx, NY 10468 USA

Preface

What are things made of?

What is the ground under our feet made of? The sun over our heads, the houses and machines, trees and bushes and flowers - and our own bodies - what are they made of?

Just look anywhere about you and you can easily count up dozens, hundreds of different things. Look at the book you are reading, for instance. It is made of paper and cardboard and cloth, printer's ink and paste.....

And the table the book is lying on. It is made of wood, covered with varnish, glued together with cabinet-maker's glue. Over in the corner is the cast iron radiator. On the walls there is whitewash made of chalk to cover up the rough plaster and bricks. You'll find two kinds of glass in your room, that in the windows and that in the electric light bulbs. You can add to these the copper and rubber in the electric wiring, the porcelain in the socket, ink, the steel of your pen, paint of several colours, and lots and lots of other things.

When you go outside you are surrounded with many more kinds of things. Step into a factory and try to count up all the different objects you see. Go to the woods or the mountains, or put on a diver's suit and go down to the bottom of the sea. Everywhere you will find more and more different things.

You can count up millions and tens of millions of different kinds of substances, with or without life. Take precious stones alone - there are hundreds of different ones in the earth. And there are thousands of different kinds of iron ore, of different species of trees. Of colours, both natural and artificial, there are tens of thousands.

And what a variety of qualities may be found in all these things! One substance is incredibly hard; another shatters to bits at the touch of a child's hand. One has a nice taste; another burns the tongue.

Some things are transparent, others opaque; some dull, some sparkling, some dirty gray, some snow white....

Some substances do not freeze but remain liquid at a temperature of 400° F. below zero. Others won't melt, but remain solid even in the terrific heat of an electric arc. One thing is unaffected by heat or cold or moisture or strong acids; while another, from the mere heat of your hand, will explode and fly into a thousand pieces.

Everything in nature is in continuous motion. Thousands of changes are taking place all the time in every square foot of ground. Some things are disappearing, others are taking their places.

At first glance it may seem that all this endless change is going on quite at random. You might think it a picture of confusion and disorder. As a matter of fact, that is not so at all. Long, long ago, people suspected there must be some kind of unity and simplicity behind the great variety of nature. They found out that everything in existence is made up of the same simple parts or ingredients to which they gave the name of 'elements.'

There are only a few elements, but they can form innumerable compounds and combinations. Put together, the elements make up all the enormous number of things we find in the world.

You can see something similar to this in the world of speech and sound. All our words are made up of the 26 letters in the alphabet. And thousands of different melodies are composed merely by making different combinations of the same musical tones: hymns and funeral marches, simple children's songs and complicated symphonies.

The elements were not all discovered at one time. People were familiar with many of them in ancient times. But ages passed before it was understood that they were actual elements and not compounds. And, on the other hand, some compounds were long thought to be elements, as chemists did not know how to split them up. Some elements are so rarely met with or so completely concealed from the eyes of men that it was a big job to discover them.

Scientists kept up the search for elements for hundreds of years. They spent many hours at their task and showed a great deal of ingenuity and intelligence.

You will find their story in this book. This is the tale of the most important discoveries of the elements and how they took place.

CHAPTER 1
Fiery Air

1. Karl Scheele, apothecary's apprentice

In the early half of the 17th century, there lived in Sweden an unusually industrious young apothecary. His name was Karl Wilhelm Scheele. Though he was merely an apprentice and later a laboratory assistant his great diligence and devotion to his work always amazed his employers.

His duties consisted of making up pills, medicines and plasters. But Scheele always did much more than was required of him. As soon as he had finished mixing his medicines, he would bury himself in some out-of-the-way corner or deep window seat and begin powdering, evaporating and distilling his beloved chemicals. He stayed in the laboratory day and night. He pored over old books on chemistry which even experienced apothecaries said were hard to understand. And even if he had not spent so much time in experiments which sometimes ended in unexpected explosions, this queer kind of assistant would not have been any too popular with his employers.

His hands were always scarred by alkalis and burned black by acids. He even seemed to like acrid sulphur fumes and the suffocating vapour of nitric acid.

One day Scheele made up a compound that smelled of bitter almonds. He took a sniff of its fumes to determine its exact odour. Then he tried its taste and his mouth began to feel unusually hot. No one who valued his life would ever make such an experiment today. The compound which smelled of bitter almonds was what we call hydrocyanic acid and is well known to be a deadly poison. It was a good thing Scheele swallowed only a tiny drop of it.

Scheele did not know the acid he had discovered was poisonous. But even if he had suspected it he would probably have tried it anyway. He knew of no greater joy than the discovery of a new substance, one which no one else in the world had ever seen; or the discovery of new properties in substances already familiar. He was always making new experiments and he breathlessly watched the results of each one to see what new things he could learn about nature.

Once he wrote in a letter to a friend: "How thrilling it is for an experimenter to find what he is looking for!"

Scheele experienced this happiness many a time and had only himself to thank for his good fortune too. He didn't go to any schools or universities and he had no assistants. He learned everything himself; he even taught himself to use his simple apparatus, consisting mainly of apothecaries' jars, glass retorts and dried beef bladders.

He served fourteen years as apprentice to the apothecary Bauch. And when, nineteen years later, he was elected a member of the Swedish Academy of Science, he was still only a laboratory assistant in a provincial apothecary's shop. He was still spending most of his meagre salary on books and chemical reagents, just as he had in his youth.

Scheele was a natural born chemist and, like every real chemist, he tried to find out "what things are made of."

Especially he wanted to find out just which were the simplest elements out of which all the things about us are formed. Long years of experimenting had convinced him he could never do this until he understood the real nature of fire. For hardly any chemical experiment could be carried out without heat, without fire.

When Scheele began to study the nature of fire, he soon reached the point where he asked himself what part air plays when something burns. He could learn a little about this from the books of the old chemists.

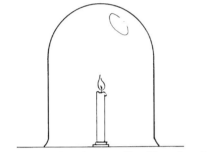

If you cover a burning candle with a glass jar, it will burn for a little while, then go out.

A hundred years before Scheele, an Englishman, Robert Boyle, as well as several other scientists, had proved that no substance can burn unless there is sufficient air. For example, if you cover a burning candle with a glass jar, it will burn for a little while, then go out. And if you extract all the air from under the jar, the candle will go out instantly.

On the other hand, if you blow more air into a fire, as blacksmiths do with their bellows, the flame gets brighter and hotter.

But no one in those days could explain exactly why this is so; precisely why air is necessary to combustion.

In order to investigate this, Scheele began to perform experiments with various chemicals in completely sealed containers. He reasoned that "there is only a limited quantity of air in a sealed container and no more can get in from the outside. So, if air has something to do with combustion and other chemical changes, this will be the easiest way to discover it."

At that time air was still considered an element - that is, a substance which could not possibly be separated into still simpler parts. Scheele shared this belief, but he was soon obliged to change his mind.

2. Why does fire go out?

Karl Wilhelm Scheele

One night Karl Wilhelm Scheele was in the laboratory of his apothecary's shop in Upsala, getting his daily experiment ready.

The building was deathly still. He had long ago shut the door behind the last customer and the owner of the shop had gone home to bed. Scheele was having a fine time all by himself with his vessels and retorts.

Out of the cupboard he took a big jar filled with water. In it was a piece of some yellow stuff that looked like wax, lying on the bottom of the jar. The water and the waxy-looking stuff at the bottom of the jar gave out a mysterious, greenish glow in the partial darkness of the room.

The stuff was phosphorous, which chemists always keep in water because when it is exposed to the air it immediately changes, losing all its usual properties. Scheele stuck a knife down into the jar and cut off a little piece of the phosphorous, without taking it out of the water. He tossed this little piece into an empty glass flask, closed the top with a cork stopper and carried it over to a lighted candle. As soon as the tip of the candle flame touched the flask the phosphorous melted and settled at the bottom in a little puddle. A second later it flared up brightly and the flask was filled with a thick mist, which quickly settled on the wall like a white frost.

It all happened in an instant. The phosphorous took fire at once and changed into dry phosphoric acid. (This acid is now called phosphoric anhydride. When it is dissolved in water the solution is called phosphoric acid. But in Scheele's time both substances were called acids.)

This was a very spectacular experiment. But Scheele seemed quite unmoved by it. It was not the first time he had set fire to phosphorus and watched it change into acid. In this case it was not the phosphorus itself he was interested in. It was quite another thing: he wanted to find out what became of the air which was in the flask when the phosphorus burned up.

As soon as it was cool Scheele turned the flask upside down and plunged it into a tub of water up to its neck. Then a strange thing happened: the water spouted up into the inverted flask and filled it one fifth full.

"Again!" Scheele muttered to himself. "The same thing again. One fifth of the air has disappeared and the water has filled up the empty space."

It was an amazing thing! No matter what substances Scheele tried burning in closed containers, he always got the same curious result: the air in the container regularly lost one fifth of its volume. Now this same thing has occurred again.

The phosphorus burned up. All the phosphoric acid remained in the flask but one-fifth of the air had escaped.

How could it get out of the tightly sealed flask?

Scheele had been getting a new experiment ready while the flask was cooling. He decided this time to try burning an even more combustible thing in a sealed container - the gas formed when metal is dissolved in acid.

It took only a few minutes to prepare the combustible gas. Scheele dropped a few filings into a little bottle, poured a solution of oil of vitriol over it and closed the bottle with a stopper which had a long glass tube inserted in it. The iron filings hissed, the acid boiled and little silvery gas bubbles formed in it. Scheele held a lighted candle at the top of the glass tube in the stopper. Instantly the escaping gas took fire and a tiny, pale tip of flame flickered at the end of the tube. (Reader, if you try to perform this experiment yourself you may cause an explosion. Before you ignite the gas, you must wait a few minutes, until the entire tube is filled with gas. Better not try such experiments by yourself, but do them under the supervision of your teacher.)

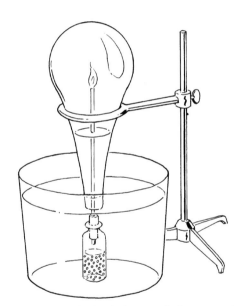

Scheele put the bottle into a tall glass vessel filled with water and inverted an empty flask over it.

Next Scheele put the bottle into a tall glass vessel filled with water and inverted an empty flask over it so that the neck of the flask was under water and no air could possibly get into it. The dim little flame of gas continued to burn in this enclosed space. The moment the flask was inverted over the flame, water began to force its way up into it. The flame continued to burn in the upper part, the water kept rising in the lower part. Higher and higher rose the water and the higher it got the more faintly the gas burned until it finally went completely out.

Scheele noticed that at this moment the water occupied about one fifth the volume of the flask.

"Well, now," he thought, "granted that the air, for some unknown reason, disappears during combustion. But why only a fifth of it? There was still gas enough left to go on burning for a long time. The iron filings are still hissing, the acid is still boiling. If I take off the flask and light the gas again in the open air it will burn once more. Why does the flame go out under the flask, when it is still four-fifths filled with air?"

Suddenly a vague theory popped into his head, one that had occurred to him several times before: "Can it be that the air left in the flask is different from that part of it which disappears during combustion?"

He was just about to begin another experiment on the spot to test this conjecture but, glancing at the clock, he regretfully gave up the idea. It was already long past midnight and he knew he would have to be at his post early next morning, mixing drugs.

So he put out his candle and reluctantly left the laboratory. But the idea about the two different kinds of air persisted in his mind. He was still thinking about it when he fell asleep.

3. Living and dead air

Next day, just as soon as he got through with the routine duties of the shop, Scheele eagerly set to work to test his new theory.

He looked over all the notes he had made in his laboratory notebook since he had begun to study fire and combustion. He repeated some of his experiments. He made the most painstaking examination of the air that remained in the flask after something had been burned in it. This air seemed to be lifeless and perfectly useless. Nothing wanted to burn in it. Lighted candles went out just as if some unseen person had blown on them. Red hot coals cooled off; a burning splinter would die out as quickly as if it had been doused with water. Even phosphorus refused to burn in it.

Scheele tried putting live mice into a jar filled with this dead air.

Scheele tried putting live mice into a jar filled with this dead air. They immediately died of suffocation.

Now this air did not look any different from ordinary air. It was just as transparent and colourless and free from any smell or taste as the air that filled the room.

Suddenly it all became clear to Scheele: ordinary air, the air that is all about us, is not an element, as people had thought from time immemorial. It is not a simple substance but a mixture of two entirely different things. One of them helps combustion, but disappears somewhere when combustion occurs. The other, the larger part, is indifferent to fire and is absolutely unaffected by burning substances. And if air consisted of this part alone, there would never have been a single spark or a single fire on earth.

Scheele was, of course, much more interested in the active part of air, the part that disappeared during burning, than in this 'lifeless' part.

"I wonder if I can get some of this active part in a pure state, separate from the 'useless' air?" he asked himself.

It turned out that he could.

He recalled that he had often been puzzled when he saw how bits of soot took fire while floating above a crucible where saltpetre (the same as is used for black gunpowder) was being melted.

"Why is it," he had wondered, "that these specks of soot ignite so easily? Is it because just that part of the air which causes combustion, rises from the bubbling saltpetre?"

For a time now he gave up all other experimentation and devoted himself to working with saltpetre. He melted it, distilled it sometimes with oil of vitriol, sometimes without, ground it up with sulphur and with coal. The owner of the apothecary's shop watched all this activity with some fear. He thought that any day he and all his worldly goods might be blown to kingdom come. For it is only a step from saltpetre to gunpowder.

But something entirely different happened. One day, when the proprietor of the shop was praising the virtues of one of his mustard plasters to a trusting customer, Scheele suddenly burst into the shop from the laboratory. He was waving an empty bottle and shouting: "Combustible air, combustible air!"

"For heaven's sake, what is the matter?" demanded the startled apothecary. Knowing how quiet and reserved Scheele was by nature, he thought something dreadful must have happened to make his assistant so excited.

"Combustible air!" Scheele exclaimed again, tapping the empty bottle he held in his hand. "Come on! I'll show you a real miracle!" And he dragged the astonished apothecary and his customer back to the laboratory with him. He took a few smouldering coals out of the brazier with a shovel, then opened the bottle and dropped some of them into it. Instantly a hot, white flame shot up from the half dead coals.

"Combustible air!" said Scheele proudly.

The apothecary and the customer looked at each other in amazement. Neither one said a word.

Next Scheele picked up a little splinter of wood, lighted it, then blew it out and dropped the splinter into another bottle of his 'combustible air.' Again the almost completely extinguished fire burst into a fierce flame.

"What kind of magic is this?" stammered the poor customer, scarcely believing his own eyes. For, as far as he could see, the bottle was absolutely empty.

"There was gas in the bottle, combustible air," Scheele tried to explain. "I got it by distilling saltpetre. Only one-fifth of common air, the air all around us, is combustible."

The customer blinked. He didn't understand a word of what Scheele was saying.

"Excuse me, Karl," said the apothecary firmly, "you're talking nonsense. Who's

Combustible air, combustible air!

going to believe there's anything in air but just air? Doesn't everybody know that all air is the same? Though I must confess your experiment with the burning stick is extremely entertaining. Could you do it again?"

Scheele easily made a smouldering splinter flare up again. But he was still unable to convince his employer. People were in the habit of thinking of air as a uniform, unchangeable element and it was hard all at once to persuade them otherwise.

To tell the truth, it still seemed strange even to Scheele that air should consist of two such dissimilar gases: combustible air and useless air, as he called them.

Yet there could be no doubt about it, especially as Scheele could make ordinary air himself, by mixing one part of the 'saltpetre' air with four parts of the 'useless' air. Candles burned quietly in this mixture. Mice breathed as easily as in ordinary air.

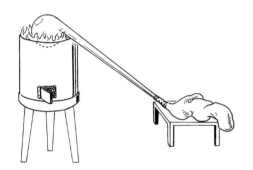

Scheele put dry saltpetre into a glass retort, placed it over a brazier and as soon as the saltpetre began to melt he held an empty collapsed, beef bladder right over the neck of the retort.

Scheele soon learned how to obtain pure combustible air by a very simple method: merely by heating saltpetre. He put dry saltpetre into a glass retort, placed it over a brazier and as soon as the saltpetre began to melt he held an empty collapsed, beef bladder right over the neck of the retort. Gradually the bladder began to swell as it was filled with the combustible air which passed into it from the retort. Then he found an ingenious way of transferring it from the bladder to whatever receptacle he wanted to put it into - a bottle or a glass or a flask.

Scheele discovered still another way of getting pure combustible air from bits of mercury oxide scalings. But the saltpetre method was the cheapest, so most of the time he used that in his experiments.

He was completely fascinated by his latest discovery. There was nothing in the world he so much enjoyed doing as watching different things burn in pure combustible air. They burned very fast and gave out a blinding glare, much more brilliant than when they burned in ordinary air. And the combustible air completely disappeared from the container during the burning.

This fact was especially noticeable when Scheele tried burning phosphorus in a sealed flask filled with combustible air. The flame flared up so brilliantly that it hurt his eyes to look at it; and later, when the flask cooled and he wanted to put it into a vessel of water, it collapsed with a deafening noise the moment he touched it, and flew into a thousand pieces.

Fortunately he was not injured and he kept his presence of mind enough to figure out what had caused the explosion: during the burning the combustible air had all been consumed and had left a complete vacuum inside the flask, so the pressure of the air outside crushed the flask, just as a nutcracker crushes an empty nutshell.

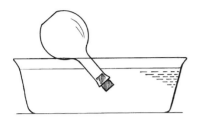

When the phosphorus had burned up and the flask was cool, he put the neck into water and tried to pull the stopper out, under water.

Next time he performed this experiment with phosphorus Scheele was more careful. He used such a strong, thick-walled flask that it could withstand the pressure of the air. This time, when the phosphorus had burned up and the flask was cool, he put the neck into water and tried to pull the stopper out, under water, to see how much of the combustible air was left. But he found it would be extremely difficult to pull the stopper out. Evidently inside the flask there was a nearly perfect vacuum and the pressure of the outside air was pushing the stopper with great force into the neck of the flask. It was as if the stopper were gripped by a powerful pair of pliers.

So Scheele decided to try pushing the stopper in. He had no trouble at all in doing this and immediately water from the vessel in which he was holding the flask upside down, rushed in and filled the glass right up to the very bottom.

So he was absolutely sure that the combustible air did disappear completely during the burning.

Scheele tried breathing pure combustible air right out of the bladder. He was not able to tell the difference between it and ordinary air. As a matter of fact, it is, of course, much easier to breathe 'combustible' air than ordinary air. That is why today we give it to ill or dying people who are having trouble with their breathing. Only we don't call it 'combustible' air. We call it oxygen.

4. The elusive phlogiston

Scheele was bent on unravelling the mystery of fire, when his researches led him to the unexpected discovery that air was not an element, but a mixture of two gases, which he called 'combustible' and 'useless' air.

This was the most important of Scheele's many important discoveries. But had he accomplished his original purpose? Had he discovered the real nature of fire? Did he understand now what fire was and what happened during combustion?

He thought he had accomplished what he set out to do. But as a matter of fact fire remained as great a mystery as ever. The root of the trouble lay in the 'phlogiston' theory, which all chemists in those days accepted as true. They thought a substance could burn only if it contained a large quantity of an inflammable stuff. This they called phlogiston.

No one knew exactly what phlogiston was. Some thought it was a kind of gas, while others said that you could not see phlogiston nor get it in a pure state, as it could not exist independently, but was always combined with some other substance.

Some scientists, it is true, did maintain for a time that they had succeeded in separating out phlogiston in its pure form, but later they themselves doubted it and announced that "what we took for pure phlogiston was not phlogiston at all."

Chemists did not know whether or not this phlogiston had weight, as everything else has. It was as elusive and without substance as a ghost. Yet all chemists in those days firmly believed in its existence.

Where did such a curious notion come from?

Everyone who has watched a fire has noticed that when anything is burned, it goes to pieces and disappears.

Everyone who has watched a fire has noticed that when anything is burned, it goes to pieces and disappears. So people concluded that something had been taken out of the burning substance and gone up in the flame, leaving behind only embers, cinders, scale, or an acid. (Nowadays we call such a product of combustion an anhydride of an acid.) It was as if the flame had driven some ghostly, elusive 'spirit of fire' out of the thing that had burned up. Therefore it was concluded that "combustion is a breaking-up of a complex inflammable substance into its fiery element, the phlogiston and its other parts."

All chemists of those days kept looking for traces of this mysterious phlogiston. A chemist would say, when he burned a piece of coal: "All the phlogiston has gone out of the coal into the air, leaving only ashes."

When phosphorus blazed up and turned into dry phosphoric acid, they explained it in the same way: "You see, the phosphorus has disintegrated into its component parts - phlogiston and phosphoric acid."

When metals rusted because of subjection to great heat or from exposure to moisture, chemists of those days fancied it was the result of the workings of phlogiston. They would say, "The phlogiston is all gone and all that is left is rust or scales."

This phlogiston theory enabled scientists of the 18th century to give quite satisfactory explanations of many natural phenomena and technical processes which otherwise seemed quite without explanation. For a long time this theory helped chemists in their researches and they never doubted its correctness.

Karl Scheele, too, firmly believed it and in his numerous experiments was always trying to figure out what became of the phlogiston. When he discovered his 'combustible' air he immediately concluded: "This air evidently is very strongly attracted to phlogiston. It is ready to rob any burning substance of its phlogiston. That is why everything burns so willingly and quickly in it."

"Useless air, on the other hand," he reasoned, "does not readily combine with phlogiston and therefore it extinguishes fire."

Remember how astonished Scheele was that during combustion the fiery air escaped from a tightly closed vessel? With or without phlogiston the fiery air somehow always disappeared.

Where did it go and how did it get out of a sealed container?

Scheele racked his brains over this riddle for a long time and finally thought up an explanation:

"When a substance burns," he said, "the released phlogiston unites with the fiery air and this invisible compound is so light that it oozes through the glass wall of the flask without being noticed, just as water soaks through cloth.

Like some fantastic spook that goes freely through stone walls and closed doors....

You see to what a queer conclusion Scheele's great faith in phlogiston brought him.

However, if he had made a thorough search for his fiery air inside the flask, he would in all likelihood have found it there. But he would first have had to get rid of the phlogiston theory and, with all his genius, he was unable to do that.

It was another great scientist of the 18th century who finally put an end to phlogiston. He was Antoine Lavoisier, a Frenchman. And once this was done, the mysterious disappearance of fiery air, as well as many another hard-to-explain phenomenon immediately lost all their mystery.

5. Antoine Lavoisier and his assistant

Antoine Lavoisier
(1743 - 1794)

Three different scientists discovered fiery air at almost the same time. Of the three, Scheele was the first to make this discovery. A year or two later Joseph Priestley, an Englishman who knew nothing at all about Scheele's discovery, discovered fiery air too; and a few months later Lavoisier, chancing on a vague hint by Priestley about a gas in which candles burned with unusual brilliance, also discovered for himself the composite nature of air.

Lavoisier was the only one of the three who realised the full significance of the discovery, the real role of fiery air in nature.

Now Lavoisier had a remarkable assistant who gave him invaluable aid in all his work. As a matter of fact, Scheele and Priestley also had the same assistant, but they did not always use his services and did not attach great importance to his advice.

It was the scales that made clear to Lavoisier the real nature of fire.

Lavoisier's helper was - scales.

Whenever he started to make an experiment he always carefully weighed each substance he was going to subject to a chemical change, and at the end of the experiment he weighed it again. As he weighed, he would reason:

"This thing has lost weight, while this other is heavier. That means something has been taken from the first and has united with the second."

It was the scales that made clear to Lavoisier the real nature of fire. They explained to him what had become of the fiery air during combustion. (Lavoisier called it 'vital' air.)

Scales revealed to him which substances were complex and which were simple, as well as many other valuable facts.

Lavoisier, like Scheele, tried burning phosphorus in a sealed flask. But he did not waste his time trying to figure out in his mind what had become of one-fifth of the air in the flask after the phosphorus had burned. His scales gave him an absolutely accurate answer to this question. Before he put the piece of phosphorus into the flask and set fire to it, he weighed it. And when the phosphorus had burned up, he again weighed the dry phosphoric acid which remained in the retort.

And which do you think was the heavier - the original phosphorus or what was left of it after burning?

Scheele and all other chemists of that time would have answered without looking at the scales: "Of course the phosphoric acid is lighter than the phosphorus was before it burned, because the phosphorus went to pieces and lost its phlogiston. And in any case, even if you admit that phlogiston has no weight, the phosphoric acid will weigh just the same as the phosphorus did before it burned."

But it turned out that this was not so at all.

The scales announced that the white frost-like powder that had settled on the sides of the flask weighed more than the original phosphorus from which it had come.

How were they to explain the fact that the phosphorus had lost its phlogiston and yet had grown heavier? This sounded as ridiculous as if someone were to maintain that a pitcher weighs more when it is empty than when it is full to the top with water.

And where do you suppose the dry phosphoric acid did get its extra weight?

"From the air!" was Lavoisier's answer.

Exactly that part of the air which seemed to have disappeared from the flask had actually not disappeared at all, but had merely united with the phosphorus while it was burning. And the acid was the result of this combination. (We now call this substance phosphoric anhydride.)

So the mysterious disappearance of the 'fiery' air was explained as simply as that. One riddle helped to solve another.

Lavoisier realised that burning phosphorus was not an exception. His experiments proved that every time anything burned, or whenever a metal rusted, the same thing happened. So he tried the following experiment:

He put a piece of tin in a vessel and closed the vessel tightly so that nothing could possibly get into it. Then he took a big magnifying glass and directed the burning rays of the sun on the tin which first melted in the heat then began to rust, to turn into a kind of scaly, grey powder.

Now, Lavoisier had weighed the air and the tin in the vessel before he began the experiment. When it was finished he again weighed the resulting powder and the left-over air. And what do you think had happened? The powder had gained exactly as much weight as the air had lost.

It was impossible for anything to have got into the vessel from outside, except the sun's rays. There had been absolutely nothing in the vessel except the piece of tin and the air. Yet the tin had grown heavier when it turned to rust. How could anyone, after this, deny that rust was the result of the combination of the tin with the 'fiery' or 'vital' part of the air?

Lavoisier also burned a piece of pure charcoal in a closed vessel, filled with 'vital' air. And when the charcoal had burned there appeared to be nothing left of it except a tiny, almost unnoticeable pinch of ashes. But, the scales told another story. They showed that the air in the vessel had grown heavier, exactly as much heavier as the burned charcoal had weighed. This indicated that the charcoal had not disappeared when it burned up, but had formed, in combination with the 'vital' air, a new substance. Lavoisier named this heavy gas carbonic acid or carbonic acid gas.

When Lavoisier described his experiments and boldly said what he thought about them, almost all the other chemists came out in opposition to him.

"What!" they said. "Do you mean to assert when something burns, or something rusts, that it is not destroyed, not broken up into various parts, but that on the contrary it has united with 'vital' air?"

"That's just what I mean to assert," Lavoisier answered. "That's precisely what I think has happened."

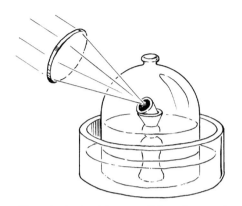

Then he took a big magnifying glass and directed the burning rays of the sun on the tin.

I don't know anything about any phlogiston.

"And what, pray, according to your theory, has become of the phlogiston during the combustion?" they asked him.

"I don't know anything about any phlogiston," Lavoisier replied. "I never saw any. My scales have never given me any sign of its existence. I take a simple, combustible substance such as phosphorus, or a pure metal such as tin and I burn it in a sealed vessel where there is nothing except the purest vital air. As a result of the combustion both the substance and the vital air disappear. In their place there appears in the vessel something entirely new - in one case phosphoric acid, in the other, tin rust. I weighed these new substances and it turns out that the one which has been formed during combustion weighs precisely as much as the weight of the phosphorus or tin plus the amount of vital air previously in the retort. This is as clear as that two and two make four. It's simply nonsense to drag in phlogiston."

This announcement raised a storm in the scientific world. Chemists were so accustomed to see the invisible signs of phlogiston everywhere that they could not possibly understand how it could suddenly disappear from the scene. It seemed to them simply nonsense to assert that when something burned it was not destroyed but, on the contrary, had attracted the 'vital' air to itself. Hadn't everyone known from childhood how destructive fire was?

At first they only laughed at Lavoisier. Then they began to belittle his works, to say that his scales lied.

But facts are stubborn things. Lavoisier kept on bringing out new and more convincing disproof of the theory of phlogiston. He produced facts which everyone could test for himself and thus be convinced of their correctness. And, under the pressure of these indisputable facts, the supporters of the phlogiston theory gradually began to yield ground. A number of chemists made attempts to reconcile the new discovery with the phlogiston theory, suggesting one fanciful idea after another, and offering all kinds of improbable explanations.

But finally Lavoisier's views won out. The backers of the phlogiston theory laid down their arms one after another and acknowledged:

"It is hard to fight against the obvious. Lavoisier is right!"

By the end of the 18th century phlogiston was once and for all driven out of the science of chemistry.

6. A purging of the elements

The discovery of fiery or vital air and the fall of the phlogiston theory revolutionised all chemistry. Chemistry took on a different aspect. It had only now become possible to find out what are the elements of which the world about us is really composed.

Which substance was to be considered the more complex, which the simpler, phosphorus or phosphoric acid? Carbon or carbonic acid? Metal or metal rust?

Before Lavoisier, all chemists had said: "Why, of course, phosphorus is more complex than phosphoric acid. Of course metal is more complex than its rust. Phosphorus consists of two elements, phlogiston and phosphoric acid. Tin consists of two elements, phlogiston and tin rust." And so on and so on.

Now, when it had turned out that these substances did not lose anything during combustion but, on the contrary, gained a new element, 'fiery' air, everything had to be looked at in a different light.

Phosphorus had to be regarded as the pure element, phosphoric acid as the compound, since the latter is formed by the combination of phosphorus and 'fiery' air, while it is impossible to break up phosphorus into any other substances.

Pure carbon was acknowledged to be an element, carbonic acid was not.

Lavoisier announced that all metals were elements and that their rusts were compounds. Furthermore, the newly discovered 'fiery' air and 'useless' air were found to belong to the ranks of the elements. Lavoisier called the first oxygen, acid maker, because it forms acids with a number of combustible substances: dry phosphoric acid with phosphorus, carbonic acid with carbon, sulphuric acid with sulphur... He named the 'useless' air azote, from a Greek word meaning lifeless.

Elements

~~Air~~

~~Water~~

Oxygen

Hydrogen

Azote

...

Up to this time water had been considered an element. From the most ancient times scientists and philosophers had always begun their list of elements with air and water. You have just learned how air was shown to be a mixture and not an element. Well, about ten years after the discovery of the composite nature of air, it was water's turn. First an Englishman, Cavendish, and a little later Lavoisier, proved that water was not an element at all, but a compound.

Imagine how astonished people were. Water, just ordinary water, turned out to consist of 'vital' air, or oxygen, and another element which Lavoisier named hydrogen (water maker). Hydrogen is a very light combustible gas given off when a metal is dissolved in acid.

So water too, like air, had to be struck off the list of elements.

After this Lavoisier tried to count up all the elements there were on the earth. He listed more than thirty. According to him, then, all the countless, complex things in the world were composed of these thirty or so elements. But he was very doubtful about some of those substances he had listed as elements.

"I am compelled to regard them as elements," he confessed," only because we have not as yet been able to separate them into their component parts. There is much reason to believe that they are, in fact, compounds. The time will come when chemists will find the means to prove this quite as surely as we have now established the compound nature of air and water."

Lavoisier's prophecy came true to the letter, and very soon. We will discover in the next chapter how this came about.

CHAPTER 2
Chemistry and Electricity form an Alliance

1. Volta piles

At the very beginning of the 19th century two Italian scientists, Luigi Galvani and Alessandro Volta, made a very important discovery, namely, that electricity could flow, could go round and round a closed circuit without stopping and for a long time.

Galvani was the first to observe this, but it was Volta who found the correct explanation. Volta built the first apparatus for producing an electric current. He did this during the last years of the 18th century and from that moment a new epoch in the history of science and technology began.

The Volta apparatus was very simple: a circular piece of zinc was placed on a similar piece of silver or copper. He found that he could even use ordinary silver or copper coins. Next came a similar disk made of cardboard, leather, or cloth, which had been soaked in salt water. On top of this he placed a silver and next a zinc disk, then again a piece of damp leather and so on for ten, twenty, or thirty layers in succession - silver, zinc, damp leather.

Thus he constructed a pile or as it was called later, a 'Volta pile.'

This simple arrangement of metallic and non-metallic disks piled in this order, one on top of another, always produced a steady flow of electricity.

Volta's pile could be made in another way too: by laying it on its side, as it were. Ten, twenty, or any other number of glass jars filled with salt water, or dilute acid were placed in a row, one after another. At one side of every jar a copper plate was suspended and at the other side, a zinc one. Then the entire row of jars was made into one whole by connecting a copper plate of one jar to a zinc plate in the following jar.

A battery like this took up much more room than the pile of little disks, but in return it was much more powerful.

Anyone could easily construct such a battery for himself and test the power of the new force discovered by Galvani and Volta.

It was at once recognised that the electric current would enable people to accomplish extraordinary things. In the first place it decomposed water. As soon as the circuit of one of these batteries was closed, water began to separate into its component parts. From one end an inflammable gas came out, a gas already known as hydrogen. From the other little bubbles rose; and this we already know as oxygen, Scheele's 'fiery' air.

It was also noticed that when an electric current passed through ordinary water an acid would mysteriously form on one plate, and a caustic alkali on the other. The current would not only separate the water into hydrogen and oxygen, of which water is composed, but also drew out of the water some substance which had never before been discovered in it.

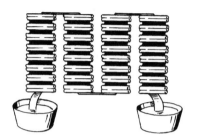

A current from a Volta pile would separate out metals from a solution made of their salts.

Some time later another discovery was made: a current from a Volta pile would separate out metals from a solution made of their salts. If, for example, crystals of blue vitriol (copper sulphate) were dissolved in water and an electric current passed through the solution, an even layer of pure copper soon began to be deposited on one of the plates. In the same way gold, silver and other metals could be separated out from their liquid solutions.

Volta's pile, the work of a physicist, turned out unexpectedly to be a powerful tool in the hands of chemists. Now, without fire or flame, silently and with the greatest precision, the electric current caused the most amazing chemical changes.

Scientific journals were unable to print the countless papers they received from scientists announcing ever new 'electrical' experiments.

Like prospectors in a gold rush when there had been a notable 'strike' in a gold field, so all the scientists rushed into the field of experimentation with Volta's pile. They expected an endless stream of miracles from it.

Among all this throng of early electro-chemists, the name of one young scientist - Humphry Davy, an Englishman - stands out head and shoulders above all the rest.

2. The childhood and youth of Humphry Davy

The year Professor Galvani first announced his discovery to the world, Humphry Davy was still just a mischievous lad, with no special love for school, who received many an ear-pulling from his teachers for his indifference to Latin and his repeated pranks. So he naturally preferred sitting by a stream with his fishing rod or roaming through the woods looking for game, to spending tedious hours in school cramming his brain with old Roman poets.

"Oh, Humphry!" his teacher, the Reverend Coriton, used to say. "He'll never set the world on fire."

Penzance, where Humphry was born and passed his childhood, was then a typical country village. It was cut off from the large towns and cities of England by bad roads. It was harder in those days to go from Penzance to London than it is now to go from the United States to Abyssinia. People did most of their travelling on horseback and an ordinary carriage was as rare a sight on the streets of Penzance as a camel would be nowadays on the streets of London.

News of what was going on in the outside world was a long time reaching Penzance and not many people in the village were interested in it when it did get there.

Boxing matches, hunting, cock-fighting and getting dead drunk were the chief amusements of the people. What was there in such an environment to arouse an interest in science in any young person? Least of all could the Reverend Coriton with his Latin.

Humphry was a regular village urchin until the age of sixteen. He was famous among his young companions for two things: his ability to reel off original poems and his marksmanship. In other respects he was just a gawky, sloppy, empty-headed village youth.

His life changed abruptly with the death of his father, who had been a wood-carver. As the eldest son in an orphaned family Humphry felt a heavy responsibility. True, there was not much he could do for the family with his verse-making, or his bad Latin, or even his skill as a fisherman and marksman.

Humphry decided to apprentice himself to the local doctor, whose name was Borlas. This doctor, like the majority of the doctors of his day, was a 'practical' doctor; that is, he had not taken any special medical studies. He had picked up what he knew about the science of healing by practising on people. At first he had worked under an older doctor and had observed what he did. Later he set up in practice for himself. This was what Humphry Davy planned to do. No one in those days thought there was anything strange in learning the trade of medicine in the same way that people learned to make boots or to shoe horses.

Now Dr. Borlas was also an apothecary. He made up his own medicines and young Davy's main work at first was to prepare powders, to dissolve salts and spices and to distil oils and acids. It was here in Dr. Borlas's shop that Humphry had his first contact with chemistry.

His story is much like that of Karl Scheele. From preparing pills and medicines Humphry went on to more complicated chemical experiments and soon became deeply interested in his new occupation. He did not entirely give up his verse-making and his fishing, but they were pushed into the background.

The family of Dr. Borlas sometimes jumped out of their beds in terror, awakened by

Dr. Borlas made up his own medicines.

the roar of an explosion, which was the result of the zealous apprentice's investigations into the secrets of chemistry.

Now Humphry realised, for the first time, that he was ignorant and began to make up for lost time in earnest. He mapped out a programme of self-education for himself which included the learning of not less than seven languages, living and dead, and the study of about twenty different branches of science, from anatomy to philosophy.

This was anything but a modest programme for a sixteen-year-old boy. But Davy displayed unexpected qualities. He acquired everything in a flash. He would gulp down a thick tome as if it were just an amusing story. His friends were amazed at the way he mastered the contents of serious books which he seemed only to have skimmed through. After a year or two his former teacher was compelled to confess that he had made a big mistake in sizing up his mischievous pupil. The best educated people of Penzance and the surrounding country became enthusiastic admirers of Davy's erudition and his ingenious experiments.

His fame soon spread beyond the limits of Penzance. In 1798, when he was only twenty years old, he was invited to go to Bristol to work in the Medical Pneumatic Institution, where a certain Professor Beddoes was experimenting in the treatment of the sick with nitrogen, hydrogen, oxygen and other recently discovered gases.

Here Davy carried on many interesting experiments. He discovered 'laughing gas' - a gas which excited and intoxicated like wine. This discovery made him famous all over England.

One fine day Davy received a letter from London. The Royal Scientific Institution invited him to work there.

The name 'Royal' did not mean that the King of England was the head of this institution or took any part whatever in its work. The King had scarcely any connection with it. He did not even give it a penny. A group of private benefactors supported it from their own means and by soliciting gifts from rich men. The King only 'graciously' permitted himself to be inscribed as one of the founders of this scientific institution; therefore it was called 'Royal'.

Naturally young Davy was delighted with this invitation and hastened to send his acceptance.

In the report of a session of the Royal Institution of February 16, 1801, we read: "Mr. Humphry Davy was employed by the Royal Institution as assistant to the professor of chemistry, director of the laboratory and assistant editor of the Journal of the Institute. His salary is to be 100 guineas per year, with lodgings, coal and candles supplied free."

Humphrey Davy
(1778 - 1829)

3. The Institution on Albemarle Street

The idlers of so-called high society of London suddenly discovered a new form of amusement - visiting the lectures on chemistry at the Royal Institution.

There was a war going on just then between England and France, so it was impossible for these fashionable people to make their usual visits to gay Paris. Where were they to find amusement?

A rumour spread about that a new professor had come to the Institution on Albemarle Street and that his lectures were quite unique. Frivolous ladies and stout gentlemen, bored to death in their drawing rooms and clubs, rushed to get tickets for these lectures.

Never before had London society taken up chemistry as an amusement.

The first thing they noticed when they entered the hall on Albemarle Street was a big table covered with all kinds of apparatus. An experienced eye would at once have noticed tall Volta piles from which spirals of wire projected in all directions.

At the appointed hour the door opened and in walked the new professor. The ladies raised their lorgnettes, the gentlemen stretched their necks to get a good view.

They saw a tall young man of twenty-six standing on the platform before them. He had a rather small head, with thick chestnut hair and a remarkably vivacious, intelligent expression in his eyes.

"How young he is!" people whispered to one another.

This was Professor Humphry Davy, the son of a village wood-carver, the very same Humphry who, a few years ago, had run about the streets of Penzance with his fishing tackle in his hands and his pockets full of worms. Now here he was delivering lectures before the most exclusive set in London society!

Davy, nervous and restless, hastened from one instrument to another. He connected and disconnected the galvanic circuits, showed how blue litmus turned red as soon as an acid appeared on the plate of the electric batteries; how, right before their eyes, certain substances disappeared and others took their place.

His lively treatment made difficult theories simple and clear. He spoke with passion and eloquence. At times it seemed as if it were not a scientist but a poet declaiming his own poetry.

Few preachers or political orators have ever spoken so warmly, so convincingly, so passionately, as Davy the chemist spoke about his experiments.

His lectures were a huge success. The hall was always packed. The audience frequently burst into applause, and the ladies sent him flowers and wrote him fan letters.

He was constantly invited to the most fashionable houses; and he accepted the invitations. Scrubbing the chemical stains from his hands, he would put on an evening suit and hurry off to a big dinner or ball. This gifted research worker, this learned man, this poet of science, spent too many hours in drawing rooms, wasting his precious time.

But his genius and his youth made up for it. When he worked he threw himself so whole-heartedly into what he was doing that he accomplished a great deal in the few hours he had left for work.

What did he do at the Royal Institution?

The governors of the Institution called on him for the most unexpected services. For instance, they asked him to deliver a course of lectures on the tanning of leather for the benefit of men engaged in the tanning industry.

"But I was never in a leather works in my life," Davy objected.

"That doesn't matter," they replied. "You know your chemistry anyway."

There was nothing to do but take up the study of tanning leather.

So there was nothing to do but take up the study of tanning leather. He was so quick at learning all about any subject to which he turned his attention and so interested always in his work, that in a short time he was very successful even in this field. He discovered that leather could be tanned by the use of a special tree sap, catechu, and he taught tanners to use it in their tanneries.

But the governors of the Institution soon thought up something new for him to do. They asked him to arrange the Institution's large collection of minerals. So he had to analyse all the different minerals in the collection.

Then they put him to work at agro-chemistry, the chemistry of agriculture. He began a round of visits to the landlords' estates and the farms of the peasants. He dug around in the mud and clay, studied manures and talked with old farmers about their crops.

He did all these things somewhat unwillingly. His own speciality was electro-chemistry and he begrudged the time spent on other kinds of work.

Back in the days at Bristol, in the Pneumatic Institution, he had mastered the use of the Volta pile and had made many experiments with it. And now, when he had the laboratory of the Royal Institution at his disposal, he began to construct one battery after another, each one more powerful than the last. Some of them had a hundred or more sets of plates.

He was especially curious about the chemical changes produced by an electric current.

Where did the acids and alkalis come from that appeared in ordinary water when an electric current was passed through it? That was the question that interested him most during his earlier days in the laboratory.

Step by step he was able to get the answer. He said it was a mistake to think, as some people did, that alkalis and acids could be manufactured out of nothing. He insisted that they must come from the glass of the jar, or from minute particles of the metal of the plates and that the electric current attracted all kinds of foreign matter. The current then deposited these impurities in the form of acids and alkalis on the plates (through which the current was passed) suspended in the water.

In order to prove his contention that the acids and alkalis came from impurities he tried the following experiment. He made a battery using a vessel of pure gold filled with distilled water. He placed this battery under a glass cover and pumped out all the air so there could not possibly be any foreign substances anywhere. Then he turned on the electric current. Bubbles of hydrogen and oxygen immediately appeared but there was not a sign of acids or alkalis.

Davy reported this experiment to the Royal Institution on the 20th of November, 1806.

The lecture in which he made this report was called the Bakerian lecture, because a certain Mr. Baker, a dealer in antiques and an amateur scientist, had, at his death, left the Royal Institution 100 pounds sterling in trust, with the provision that every year the accrued interest should be given to some scientist to deliver a lecture, to be called the Bakerian lecture, on some important scientific discovery.

This is a widespread custom in various countries and quite a number of wealthy individuals have thereby sought to purchase fame that they could gain in no other way.

At the beginning of the 19th century it was considered a high honour to be asked to deliver the annual Bakerian lecture. It was in 1806 that this honour was first conferred on Davy and he made so great an impression on the scientific world, both in England and abroad, that a gold medal was conferred on him in France, although that country was at war with England at the time. Davy's discovery was hailed as the most important since Volta's.

But this was only the beginning. Exactly one year later Davy again delivered the

The Royal Institution's
Bakerian Lecture
to be given by

***Professor
Humphrey Davy***

*on the 20th Day of
November, 1806*

Bakerian lecture at the Royal Institution and this time the honourable members of the Institution heard something that was really incredible - namely that three new chemical elements had been discovered.

And what elements!

4. Caustic potash and caustic soda

Among the many things chemists had long used in their laboratories two caustic alkalis, caustic potash and caustic soda, occupied an important place.

Hundreds of different chemical reactions were produced in laboratories, in factories, and in daily life by these alkalis. For example, with these alkalis solutions could be made of substances which were generally insoluble and with their help the strongest acids and most suffocating vapours could be freed of all their burning and poisonous properties.

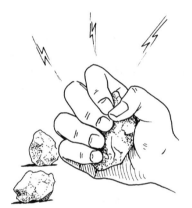

Pick up a piece of caustic soda or caustic potash and try squeezing it in your hand.

Caustic alkalis are very singular substances. In appearance they are not at all unusual. They look like whitish, rather hard pieces of rock. But pick up a piece of caustic soda or caustic potash and try squeezing it in your hand. You'll get a slight burning sensation, about the same as if you had grasped a nettle. If you hold it long enough it will become extremely painful and finally your skin and flesh will be eaten to the bone.

That is why they are called caustic, to distinguish them from other less harmful alkalis, such as ordinary soda and potash. Caustic soda and caustic potash were usually obtained from ordinary soda and potash.

These caustic alkalis have a powerful attraction for water. If you leave a perfectly dry piece of caustic soda or caustic potash in the air, the surface will soon be covered with moisture. In a short time it will become soft and porous and finally it will be just a shapeless, fluid mass

This is because the alkali has attracted water vapour from the air and formed a solution with it.

If a person sticks his fingers into a solution of caustic alkali he exclaims in astonishment: "Why it's just like soap!"

And that is precisely right, it is slippery like soap. That, in fact, is why soap feels 'soapy', because it is made with alkali. And a solution of caustic alkali also tastes like soap.

But a chemist does not recognise a caustic alkali by its taste but by the way it acts with litmus and with acids. A piece of paper soaked in blue litmus turns red the instant it is dipped in an acid; and if this red paper is then dipped in alkali it instantly turns blue again.

Caustic alkalis and acids cannot live side by side in peace for a single second. A violent reaction is set up at once. They sizzle, get hot and one counteracts the other until one of them is completely used up. Only then do peace and quiet reign.

The technical expression for this is that alkali and acid 'neutralise' each other. If they are combined the resulting mixture is a 'neutral' salt, neither alkaline nor acid. For example, ordinary cooking salt is formed by the combination of hydrochloric acid with caustic soda.

For a chemist in Davy's time, just as for a contemporary chemist, caustic alkalis were very useful, reactive agents. Every laboratory worker made their acquaintance right away and it was a rare day when he did not use them in his work.

It was thought that caustic alkalis were simple, indivisible substances. They combine with all kinds of other substances but it was thought to be utterly impossible to break them down into simpler substances. They were, therefore, considered elements like metals, sulphur, phosphorus and the newly discovered gases - oxygen, hydrogen and nitrogen.

Humphry Davy wanted to see the disintegrating effect of an electric current on these familiar substances.

5. The secret of the lilac flame

This idea came into Davy's mind when he saw how easily an electric current decomposed chemicals, even those tiny particles of foreign matter that chanced to be in a galvanic battery.

"Perhaps," he thought, "many of the things we have up to now considered indivisible elements will not be able to withstand an electric current."

A galvanic battery

He began a critical study and comparison of the properties of sulphur, phosphorus, carbon, alkalis, magnesia, lime and clay. Were these substances elements or not? And, if they were not elements, what unknown substances did they contain?

An interesting puzzle and well worth working at!

For several reasons Davy decided to begin with caustic alkalis. In many ways they acted like substances known to be compounds. That being the case, he reasoned, maybe alkalis are compounds too.

Remember Lavoisier's prophetic belief that some things known as elements were, in fact, compounds? Lavoisier had been unable to prove it and other chemists did not agree with him; but if so keen a chemist as Lavoisier has suspected the alkalis, then it was logical to begin with them.

When Davy made his first test with caustic potash he began by making a solution of it in water. Then he ordered his assistant, Edmund, who was also his cousin, to assemble and connect together all the electricity-producing apparatus in the Royal Institution. It was an imposing array: 24 big sets with zinc and copper plates a foot square; 100 with plates six inches square; 150 with plates four inches square. This combined battery gave a powerful current and Davy hoped the caustic potash would be unable to withstand it and would separate into its component parts. They poured some of the colourless, transparent alkaline solution into a vessel, then let two wires connected with the galvanic battery down into it.

As soon as the electric current passed through the solution bubbles of gas appeared on the wires. In a short time the solution began to sizzle and grow hot and the bubbles rose faster and faster to the surface.

"That's the water separating into hydrogen and oxygen gas," said Davy in a disappointed voice. "Let's see what happens next."

But nothing else happened. The current decomposed the water of the solution into hydrogen and oxygen, but the caustic potash remained unaffected.

However, Davy was not a man to give up at the first set-back.

"Well then," he thought, "if water is a hindrance, let's try it without water."

So he decided to try melting the alkali, instead of making a solution of it. He sprinkled a little dry caustic potash into a platinum spoon and held it over a spirit lamp and, using bellows, blew previously prepared oxygen into the flame. This made the flame burn fiercely and in about three minutes an incandescent wash of caustic potash spread over the bottom of the spoon. To the spoon he connected one end of the galvanic circuit and stuck the other end into the red hot alkali.

The caustic liquid began to smoke a little and threw out sharp-pointed, fiery sparks. Davy was too excited to notice the pain of the burns they made on his hands. His only thought as he held the platinum wire to the surface of the molten alkali was, "Is it going to separate or not? There's no water this time. Nothing but the alkali in the spoon. If it is not an element it's got to show its colours now...."

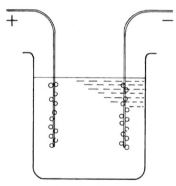

As soon as the electric current passed through the solution, bubbles of gas appeared on the wires.

Or maybe the current won't go through the molten alkali?"

But, yes, the current went through it.

"Look here!" Davy called out in an excited voice. "Come here, Edmund! I'll bet it's going to separate!"

His assistant came up holding one hand over his eyes to protect them from the sparks. But Davy was watching so intently that he almost stuck his nose into the spoon.

The electric current was obviously having an effect on the molten alkali. A slender tongue of flame of an unusually beautiful rosy lilac colour shot up from the point where the platinum wire touched the molten alkali. It continued to burn as long as the current was on but the instant the electricity was turned off the flame died out. The assistant glanced in amazement at his chief.

"What does that mean?" he asked.

"That, my dear Edmund, means we have found an impostor element," said Davy emphatically. "The current has separated some unknown substance out of the alkali. That was what gave the lilac-coloured flame at the end of the wire. No other explanation is possible. But what it is and how I am going to trap it, I don't yet know myself."

It did look as if it were not going to be an easy thing to single out the mysterious substance.

Did it really exist? Wasn't Davy attaching too much importance to that tiny, lilac-coloured bit of flame at the end of the platinum wire?

A less ardent experimenter than Davy, Luigi Galvani, once said very wisely: "The investigator, when he is making an experiment, often sees what he wants to see rather than what is really there."

Perhaps Davy was only seeing in the spoon what he was so eager to see?

He repeated the experiment several times and every time, without exception, the little lilac flame appeared as soon as the upper wire was attached to the negative pole of the battery and the platinum spoon to the positive pole. If this order was reversed there was no flame, but there were other signs of decomposition of the alkali: bubbles of some gas rose from the bottom of the spoon and burst into flame at the surface one after the other. This appeared to be hydrogen. As to the unknown substance which burned with the lilac flame, he was unable to capture it, no matter how he tried.

6. "A magnificent experiment"

One foggy October morning Davy hurried down to his laboratory after a hasty breakfast in his room.

Today he was going to make one more trial. The first experiment had failed because of the water. The second time the trouble was that the temperature of the molten, red-hot alkali was too high.

This indicated, then, that he must try to extract the unknown substance without water, but without fire too, because the unknown substance burned up the moment it appeared. If he could dispense with fire then he might win success.

But how was he going to melt caustic potash without fire? Why not try passing the electric current through a solid, cold piece?

Why not try passing the electric current through a solid, cold piece?

This was the plan Davy had in mind that chilly October morning. The evening before he had returned late from a ball and had only had about three hours' sleep, so he was not feeling any too well. But as soon as he began to work, his low spirits vanished and he set about the experiment with his usual enthusiasm. Edmund soon arrived to help him.

The problem was how to make the electric current pass through the cold potash. Davy knew that cold potash in dry form is an insulator like glass or phosphorus and that electricity would not pass through it. That was the reason he had made a water solution in his first experiment only to find that the electric current merely decomposed the water and had no effect whatsoever on the potash.

He worked with the stubborn caustic potash for hours on end but got nowhere. If he kept the water away from the alkali the current would not pass through it, even when it was turned on full force. Yet he had no success at all when he used water.

But he did not give up. He forgot everything else in the world. A little piece of white potash was constantly before his eyes: indivisible, defying everybody and everything.

"Whatever happens, I've simply got to decompose that alkali!"

A dozen new plans occurred to him, but they were all either too complicated or had too little chance of success.

"I've simply got to make that current go through a solid piece of alkali somehow," he finally resolved. "Edmund, let's try once more. Get me another piece of potash."

Edmund took another perfectly dry piece of potash out of the jar. But before he put it on a leaf of platinum which was connected with the negative end of the battery, Davy held it a minute, only a minute, in the air.

"We'll try letting it get just a tiny bit of moisture from the air this time. Maybe that will be just enough to make it a conductor of electricity," he reasoned aloud. "So minute a quantity of water will probably not prevent the current from decomposing the alkali."

It was a clever idea. It would not do to have it wet and it would not do to have it dry; so he decided to try a piece that was neither wet nor dry.

The piece of potash showed only a faint layer of moisture on its surface when Davy placed it on the platinum and touched it on top with a platinum wire, thus closing the circuit.

The current passed through!

The hard lump of alkali began to melt instantly from the top down towards the bottom. Davy trembled with excitement and hardly dared breathe as he watched the experiment. The alkali was melting at the point of contact with the metal. It was sizzling gently.

Seconds seemed like ages.

Suddenly there was a crackle, something like a small explosion. Davy gave his assistant a violent nudge with his elbow as he hovered over the experiment.

"Edmund ... Edmund ... Look, Edmund," he whispered.

The melting potash was beginning to bubble more and more on the surface. Underneath, on the platinum leaf, minute globules were seen coming out of the molten alkali. The globules had a silvery sheen and resembled pellets of mercury, but they acted differently. Some exploded and disappeared almost as soon as they appeared. The ones that remained, rapidly tarnished in the air and were soon covered with a white film.

It looked as if there was some kind of metal in caustic potash! Up to this moment no one had ever suspected such a thing.

Davy jumped up like a crazy man and began to prance about the laboratory in his joy. Something came crashing down from a shelf. An empty retort collided with an iron tripod and broke into a thousand pieces. An attendant over in a corner of the laboratory busily filling a bottle with distilled water, rushed out of the laboratory grasping his bottle, half frightened to death.

"Hurrah, hurrah!" shouted Davy. "Bravo, Humphry! You've done it at last!"

Bravo, Humphry! You've done it at last!

He threw his arms around his cousin's shoulders, shook him and dragged him away from the table.

"Shut off the current, Edmund!" he shouted. "We've got what we wanted. Do you see the meaning of what we've just done?"

"I certainly do, Humphry, and I congratulate you with all my heart!"

It took Davy a long time to settle down. He was intoxicated with his victory.

"This is only the beginning," he said to his assistant. "Now for the other elements! Nothing can stand up against a galvanic current. We'll turn the whole science of chemistry upside down!"

It was no use to think of work any more that day. Davy was too wild with joy. When he had quieted down a little he sat down at his writing desk and opened the laboratory record book. Making blots all over the page and breaking quill after quill in his excitement, he wrote down in detail all the events of that day. Then he hastily washed his hands and started out of the laboratory singing at the top of his voice.

Just as he reached the door he stopped suddenly, turned around and went back to his desk. He opened the book again and on the margin of the page where he had set down the result of his latest experiment he wrote in big, black letters: "A magnificent experiment!"

7. A metal that floats on water and burns on ice

No one can blame Davy for his exuberant rejoicing that day. He had been dreaming about decomposing caustic alkali for many months. He had been disappointed over and over. And suddenly the impossible was accomplished. The thing that had been considered non-separable was separated.

He struck caustic potash off the list of elements and put in its place a new, hitherto unknown substance, a genuine element which he named potassium.

Davy had always been an impetuous and rapid worker. But now he displayed really incredible energy. He was wild with impatience to get together enough of the new element so that he could make a thorough study of it.

But this was not so easy. Potassium turned out to have the most unusual properties. To begin with, it was stubbornly opposed to remaining in its 'pure' state. It no sooner appeared than it tried to disappear again, to combine with other things. It took Davy's ingenuity to devise a means of preserving it for any considerable length of time.

If it did not explode or burn up the moment it emerged from the molten potash, it changed instantly when exposed to the air. It lost its brightness in a few minutes right before one's eyes and was covered with a white film. There was no use trying to scale this film off, for the bare metal was again instantly covered with a new film. This film grew moist and crumbly, and in a short time there was nothing left of the silvery metal except a shapeless, fluid mess. You had only to touch this with your finger to realise that it was our old friend caustic potash again. It felt like soap and red litmus paper immediately turned blue in it.

It was evident from this that potassium greedily gobbled up oxygen and water vapour from the air so as to return to its original state and again become an alkali.

Davy tried throwing potassium into water. Now you would think any metal would immediately sink to the bottom if you threw it into water. Anyway that was what happened with all the metals Davy knew.

Not so with potassium.

This metal did not sink but bustled round on the surface of the water.

This metal did not sink but bustled round on the surface of the water making a loud hissing noise. It soon exploded with a bang and a lilac flame appeared above the potassium. The metal kept this up, growing smaller and smaller all the time, until finally it had all turned into caustic alkali and dissolved in the water.

No matter where Davy put this 'incorrigible' element, it inevitably started a hubbub and a fire. Even when it apparently got along peacefully with some other substance, it would gradually drive other elements out of the compound and take their places itself.

It flamed up in acids; it ate into glass. If it was put into pure oxygen it blazed up with a blinding white glare that was impossible to look at. It always found traces of water in alcohol or ether and immediately combined with them. It fused easily and quickly with all metals. It combined with sulphur and phosphorus, bursting into flame as it did so. It burned even on ice and kept making holes in it, and only calmed down after it had turned into alkali.

How was Davy to handle this elusive element? How capture it? What was he to do? Where and how preserve it?

Finally, when he had almost given up all hope of discovering anything that could stand up against potassium, he found it.

Kerosene.

Potassium was perfectly peaceful in kerosene. It was apparently indifferent to it and lay quite still in it. As soon as Davy discovered this he began to store bits of potassium in kerosene the moment he obtained them from caustic potash. This made his work much easier. He could have a supply on hand and did not have to worry that he would have to break off some experiment for lack of potassium.

But now that he could get enough of the new substance to investigate its properties, Davy began to be tormented by doubts as to whether or not it really was a metal.

On the one hand it seemed obvious that it was. When it first appeared, before exposure to the air had changed its appearance, it gleamed with a wonderful, metallic sheen, like polished silver. Furthermore, like all other metals, it was a good conductor of electricity and of heat and dissolved in liquid mercury.

On the other hand, who had ever heard of a metal that burned up in water and rusted in air in the twinkling of an eye?

Also potassium was soft, like wax and could easily be cut with a knife. And it was so light that it did not always sink, even in kerosene, which is considerably lighter than water.

Gold was twenty times as heavy, quicksilver sixteen times as heavy, iron, nine times. Even some wood was heavier than potassium.

But Davy finally decided that it was a metal.

"Of course," he thought, "it is astonishing that potassium is so light. But, come to think of it, iron is also a very light metal compared with platinum and gold. Mercury is half way between these two, lighter than platinum but heavier than iron. The whole trouble is, we have become accustomed to the old metals and know nothing at all about the existence of new ones. It is quite likely other metals besides potassium will eventually be discovered which will fill up the gap between it and iron."

Davy's prediction was later completely confirmed.

8. Six stormy weeks

The Bakerian lecture was to be delivered at the Royal Institution on November 19, 1807. Davy was to deliver it again. Who was there to dispute this honour with him? What other scientific accomplishments could surpass the discovery of potassium?

He had to prepare himself well for this lecture. He must get together a great number of interesting facts and observations. He spent the few intervening weeks making a thorough study of the new substance so that by the time of the lecture everything should be perfectly clear. He was eager, anyway, to learn all that could be found out about potassium as quickly as possible.

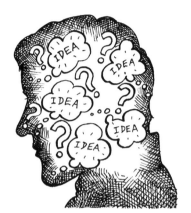

Davy had always been famous for being able to carry on several pieces of work at the same time.

He passed those six weeks in a frenzy. He had always been famous for being able to carry on several pieces of work at the same time, going from one to the other; but during this period he was a very demon of energy. His assistants and the laboratory attendants were exhausted. In a single day Davy set up 100 experiments. He rushed from the exhaust hood back to the electric batteries, from the air pump to the desk to write down the results of an experiment. In his haste he mercilessly smashed up the glass vessels in the laboratory and broke apparatus. The sound of exploding potassium alternated with the crash of broken retorts and flasks.

New theories without end popped into his head. Plans followed plans, one after another, in quick succession. He insisted on carrying out every one on the spot, no matter how much trouble it was to re-arrange all the apparatus which had been set up, for another purpose, with so much labour and pain only an hour before.

Chaos, dirt and disorder were everywhere. The laboratory looked like a stable. But, in return, by the time the day of the lecture arrived Davy knew as much about potassium as about any of the old elements which hundreds of chemists had been studying for centuries.

He founded an absolutely new branch of chemistry during the course of those six weeks. And he did not stop with potassium either.

As soon as he had succeeded in breaking down caustic potash he attacked another alkali, caustic soda. It, too, was split up by the electric current. Like caustic potash it turned out to be a compound. Like caustic potash too, it consisted of oxygen, hydrogen and some hitherto unknown metal.

This second metal was astonishingly like potassium. It also had a silvery sheen and could easily be cut with a knife, though it was a tiny bit harder than potassium. It also changed rapidly on exposure to air and ran about hissing on the top of water, though it did not have any flame as it did so. It was also quiet in kerosene, it also flamed in acids, but its flame was a dull yellow instead of lilac in colour.

In a word, Davy discovered for science two similar 'twin' elements at one and the same time. True, they do differ in some respects, but their similarities far outnumber their differences. The second metal was a little less active than the first - that's all. However, the second one was also sufficiently active to pierce holes in ice.

Davy called the second element sodium, as he got it from caustic soda.

During these six weeks, Davy kept up this hectic tempo without a pause. Only do not imagine he spent all his time in the laboratory during this period. In spite of everything he kept up his social life. Invitations were showered on him from every quarter - today a ball, tomorrow a dinner, next day both.

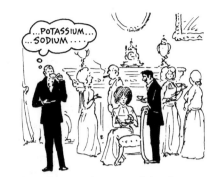

He did not neglect any of the three - potassium, sodium or fashionable drawing rooms.

And Davy, the great Davy who never for an instant stopped thinking about his wonderful twin metals, nevertheless accepted all these invitations. He did not neglect any of the three - potassium, sodium or fashionable drawing rooms. In addition to all this, he also wrote poetry; and during this time he was also called on to investigate a prison where typhus was raging. He had to find a good disinfectant to prevent the spread of the disease.

He saw prisoners kept in horrible, vermin-infested dungeons, sallow from bad air, wretched food and disease. Of what help was chemistry to them? None at all, of course. But Davy did not refuse to visit the prison as he had been requested to do.

The 19th of November, the day of the lecture before the Royal Institution, was approaching. Davy was half-dead on his feet, hollow-cheeked, his eyes sunken, his face pale. But he did not give up. He would work in the laboratory until three or four o'clock in the morning, then get up early and always be back at work before any of the others arrived. In the evening he would remember that he was to dine with some lord or other and would break his neck to be there.

"Have you noticed how our friend Davy is taking on weight?" his friends would sometimes remark to one another.

"Yes, I have. But he looked thinner again today, didn't you notice?" someone would say the next time he appeared.

The explanation of these sudden changes was simple. Davy was always in such a hurry that he could not take time to change his clothes. When he had to rush from the laboratory to a ball he did not take off the clothes he had on. He merely put fresh ones on over the others. Next day he would put on another clean shirt without taking off the soiled ones. Sometimes he would be wearing half a dozen shirts at once. When he could snatch a free moment he would take them all off at once and so grow suddenly thinner, to the amazement of his friends and acquaintances.

But very likely that is only a bit of fanciful gossip.

Finally the day of the Bakerian lecture arrived. Davy appeared and delivered the lecture as he had planned, reporting on all the recent experiments he had performed. At the end he gave a demonstration of the twin metals in action.

They dashed about on the water, exploded and produced fireworks in the air. Everyone could see for himself that they were genuine metals, as they saw them gleaming with a soft, silvery sheen in their kerosene bath.

The members of the Royal Institution were profoundly moved. The newspapers soon began to talk about Davy's recent discoveries.

"Have you heard the latest?" people were saying everywhere. "They've discovered two incredible new metals in ordinary potash and ordinary soda! They're lighter than wood, softer than wax, more combustible than coal! Next thing you know, they'll be getting gold from snuff by means of this electricity and diamonds from heaven knows where!"

The power of science had rarely been revealed more clearly and convincingly than at this time. Davy was overwhelmed by the storm of enthusiastic praise and congratulations.

9. An unexpected interruption

Davy's passion for work almost cost him his life. He had begun to feel ill a few days before the lecture. His head ached. His legs were weak and shaky. A sudden chill would come upon him at the most unexpected times - when he was working over the red hot sand bath in the laboratory, or dancing a quadrille in a room so close that the candles almost went out for lack of air and other people were dripping with perspiration.

He was unlike his usual self and felt that illness was creeping up on him; but, gritting his teeth, he had forced himself to go on working.

"What if I die before the day of the lecture and can't tell the world about my discoveries?" he had worried. "Then someone else, some foreigner, will come out and announce that he has succeeded in breaking down the alkali. No! As long as my brain will work at all and my hand can hold a pen, I'll keep on making notes of everything down to the smallest detail. Then, even if I can't deliver the lecture myself, nevertheless everything will be set down in writing and somebody else can read it for me."

However, he had been able to deliver the lecture himself. When he went on the platform he shook with fever, crimson spots burned on his cheeks, his hands trembled. But he had spoken as he never spoke before.

He had left the platform weak but happy.

Davy was unlike his usual self and felt that illness was creeping up on him.

"What's the matter?" Edmund asked anxiously, noticing that he could hardly stand on his feet.

"I think I've caught typhus," Davy muttered. "Confound that prison!"

In three or four days he collapsed completely. His condition immediately became very serious. He was consumed by fever and kept up a continual, incoherent raving. On some days, his case seemed hopeless.

The directors of the Royal Institution were greatly concerned. Of late there had been fewer and fewer donations from rich benefactors and the Institution had been depending largely on Davy's lectures which were their chief source of income. His death would be the ruination of the Institution which bore the name of His Majesty.

"How is he?" these directors would ask the doctors in a whisper as soon as one of them came out of the sick room. "How is Mr. Davy?"

How is
Mr Davy?

From all over London inquiries about his health came. His name had just become widely known. In every home and club people were talking about the amazing properties of the new metals Davy had discovered. And scarcely had the fame of the achievements of the professor of Albemarle Street been spread abroad, when an entirely different rumour followed swiftly on its heels:

"Have you heard the latest news?" Londoners asked one another. "Davy is dying!"

People thronged to the Institution, clamouring to know the smallest details. How had Professor Davy spent the night? What was his temperature? Was it true that he had got typhus while investigating conditions in the prison?

The directors of the Institution were forced to post special bulletins about his condition.

For ten weeks Davy lay burning with fever, hanging between life and death. His doctor friends took turns watching at his bedside day and night.

"Davy has no symptoms of typhus at all," they said. "He simply was overworked and his resistance was reduced to such a point that a slight cold brought him to the edge of the grave."

But he lived through it. Late in January he began to recover. He was still horribly pale and thin and weak. Work in the laboratory was out of the question. So, in order not to waste his time, he set to work to complete an unfinished poem begun some time before.

His illness had not broken him. He was the same fiery Davy, as keen of brain and quick of hand as ever. But he had to stay in bed for some time. There was not even a couch or a comfortable armchair in his poor apartment, so there was

His friends shamed the directors of the Royal Institution into buying a cheap sofa.

nowhere else to rest while he was getting well except in bed.

Oh, do not think that wealthy England did not appreciate her famous scientist. Every newspaper was full of admiration and applause for him. But a comfortable couch costs money. And the son of a village wood-carver can get along very well without a couch.

Finally his friends shamed the directors of the Royal Institution into buying a cheap sofa for three and a half guineas and it was ceremoniously installed in Davy's room. But by that time he did not need it so badly.

10. Calcium, magnesium and others

A month later experiments were again under way in the laboratory. Davy was working at top speed to make up for lost time. He had not promised to turn the chemical world upside down for nothing! There were many other suspicious elements besides the caustic alkalis. Davy wanted to test them with the electric current too.

Caustic potash and caustic soda led straight to the elements that chemists called alkaline earths: lime, magnesia, barite, strontia.

They were called earths because they enter into the composition of many kinds of earth. These earths were fire-resistant and no matter for how long they were heated they did not melt or break up or change in any way. It was impossible, or at least very difficult, to dissolve them in water.

In a word they were earths. Yet these earths were in some ways like the soapy, water-loving, caustic alkalis.

Like alkalis they readily combined with acids and neutralised them, forming harmless salts. And if with great effort they did succeed in dissolving even a small portion of any of these earths in water, the solution would instantly turn red litmus blue - one of the sure signs of alkali. That's how they happened to be called alkaline earths.

After Davy's brilliant achievement in breaking down caustic alkalis and revealing the presence of new metals in their composition, he had little doubt that he could do the same thing with the alkaline earths. He was sure there should be four fewer old elements and four more new ones. It was only a question of time. It promised to be easy to break these earths down - one should only have to moisten pieces of them with water and pass a stronger electric current through them.

Things did not go so smoothly, though, as Davy had thought they would. True, there were certain indications that the alkaline earths could be decomposed. Slight traces of some kinds of metal in the form of a light film appeared on the wires carrying the electric current. They tarnished in the air and drove hydrogen out of water, just like potassium and sodium.

But Davy could not succeed in obtaining any significant quantity of these new metals. He passed the electric current through them for hours at a time but got only minute particles of the new metals; and they were not pure metals but an alloy with the iron of the wires.

He experimented with them for a long time, until he finally wore out his big electric battery without achieving complete success.

A new, still more powerful battery was built. It had 500 pairs of plates. But still he got no results.

Finally a Swedish chemist, Berzelius, put him on the right track. He wrote Davy a letter telling him about his method of separating earths and suggested that Davy try it.

Jöns Jakob Berzelius
(1779 - 1848)

Berzelius used liquid mercury in his batteries, instead of metal wires, to conduct the electric current to the alkaline earth. He reasoned that when the metal was separated out from the earth by the electric current it would immediately dissolve in the mercury and he would get an alloy of the new metal with mercury. Now, since mercury, like water, turns to vapour when heated, one could easily get rid of it by heating and so have only the new metal left in a pure form.

Davy immediately followed Berzelius's advice and succeeded in obtaining new metals from all the alkaline earths. He called the one from lime, calcium, from the Latin word for chalk. The one from magnesia he called magnesium and he named the other two barium and strontium. They are still called by these names.

These metals are all silvery and quickly turn dull in the air. That is, they tarnish. They resolve water into its component parts, although not so energetically as potassium and sodium do. In general the alkaline earth metals occupy a place midway between the light, active metals, potassium and sodium, and the inactive, heavy old metals, iron, copper and mercury.

Davy never did get them in a perfectly pure form, even after the Berzelius letter. Much more work had to be done on each of them and he did not have the patience to go on. He proved that the alkaline earths were not elements but compounds, all containing oxygen and some metal. But this time he was not especially anxious to carry on the investigation of these new metals and study their properties. After potassium and sodium nothing could surprise him.

Davy had still less success when he tried to break down four other earths which had, up to that time, been considered elements: alumina, found in clay; silica, of which sand is composed; and beryllium and zirconium earths which chemists had only recently discovered in rare minerals.

He did not continue the study of the earths long. He gave names to the real elements which they contained, although he never succeeded in seeing them and then gave up working on them.

One earth was like another, one light metal like another. They all seemed a bit monotonous to him. He wanted to make discoveries that were unusual and astonishing.

The day of the Bakerian lecture was again approaching and Davy knew the public was eagerly awaiting his appearance. So he speeded up his work, dropped one thing and took up another that seemed to promise more effective results; dropped that in turn before it was finished and took up something else.

He even tried to break down elements whose purity it was impossible to doubt: sulphur, phosphorus, carbon, nitrogen. Davy was so eager to discover some other hidden substances in these elements that he imagined, while making the experiments, he had succeeded. Without waiting to verify his observations, he announced in his third Bakerian lecture that he had succeeded in proving that sulphur, phosphorus, carbon and nitrogen were compounds.

This was not only improbable, it was untrue. Had Davy hurried less, he would have discovered his mistakes in time and would not have denied that sulphur, phosphorus and carbon are genuine elements.

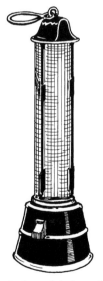

Davy invented a safety lamp for miners.

11. 'Sir' Humphry Davy

This failure did not put an end to Davy's activity as a scientist. He was only just past thirty and full of energy and initiative. In the following years he did much splendid work. He studied the properties of chlorine, which had been discovered in the 18th century by Scheele and he was the first to prove that this asphyxiating gas is an element. He invented a safety lamp for miners with which they could boldly go down underground without being afraid the fire damp would explode from its flame. This lamp, still called the Davy lamp, has saved the lives of many thousands of coal miners.

But none of his later achievements ever equalled in brilliance the results of his discovery that the caustic alkalis could be separated. The discovery of potassium and sodium marked the zenith of his scientific career.

For several years more he devoted himself to experiments with his characteristic ardour and boldness, many times even risking his own life. One day he burnt his hand with some molten potash and another time an explosion injured one eye. But he had the good luck to escape serious injuries.

As the years went by, however, Davy began to occupy himself more and more with things apart from science. Association with rich hangers-on influenced him too much. He was no longer satisfied with his humble apartment at the Royal Institution and the modest income of a professor seemed far too small.

Davy wanted wealth and social position. He did not like to be reminded that his father had been a simple artisan and that he himself had begun his career as an apprentice to a country bonesetter.

Once he thought of taking up the private practice of medicine. With his fame, he thought, there should be no lack of patients. Then his clerical friends tried to get the great scientist to join their ranks. They hoped to enlist Davy's eloquence with promises of a huge income as a servant of the church.

But Davy finally chose another way out of his difficulties: he married a rich aristocratic widow. The day before his marriage the Prince Regent knighted Davy; so from now on he proudly signed himself, 'Sir Humphry Davy.'

CHAPTER 3
Something that is both Blue and Red

1. Fifty-seven and not one more

In 1789 when Lavoisier set out to make a list of all the elements in the world, he counted up 33 in all. But as a matter of fact, only 24 of those he listed were genuine elements. The remaining 9 either did not exist in nature or were considered elements only because at that time there was no means of separating them into their component parts.

Forty years later, when Davy died, chemists were already sure of the existence of 53 different elements.

Davy himself had discovered or shown the way to discovery of 10 of the new elements. The rest were discovered by other scientists of various countries.

At the beginning of the 19th century Courtois lived in Paris. When the Napoleonic wars began in Europe and the demand for saltpetre, used in making gunpowder, increased, he built a saltpetre factory near Paris. His business prospered but he soon noticed that the copper vats in which the saltpetre was prepared were eaten through too quickly. Courtois began to investigate the cause of this and discovered an unknown caustic substance in the lyes. In its pure form it appeared as hard crystals with a dark metallic sheen. These crystals had an unusual property - when heated they immediately turned into a violet-coloured vapour instead of melting down.

Courtois gave some of this substance to his friend Professor Clément for analysis. Clément showed the stuff to the great French chemist, Gay-Lussac, and in 1813, when Davy visited Paris, he was given a piece of it to analyse.

So a new element, iodine, was discovered, the iodine we use when we want to disinfect a cut, scratch or wound. Only we do not use it in its hard form but in an alcohol solution.

A few years after the discovery of iodine, still another unknown element was discovered - a metal resembling potassium and sodium. It was very light, only slightly heavier than the very lightest kinds of wood. If this metal, like potassium and sodium, did not have the property of violent combination with water, it would make excellent life-belts, since it is so light.

This third metal, one of the family trio of alkali metals, was named lithium. A 'mate' was finally found for iodine too. In 1826 Balard, a Frenchman, discovered an unknown substance in a marsh from which salt was being obtained. It had many properties like those of iodine, but it was not iodine. When the new substance was extracted in pure form, it turned out to be a heavy, red liquid with a suffocating odour. This new element was called bromine. Everyone who is acquainted with photography knows that all photographic plates, paper and films are covered with a compound of bromine and silver. And a compound of bromine and sodium is sold in all chemist's shops as a cure for insomnia.

The Swedish scientist, Berzelius, the one who had helped Davy in 1808, discovered several new elements.

Iridium

Osmium

Rhodium

Palladium

New elements were discovered also among the precious metals. Hitherto only three precious metals were known: gold, silver and platinum. Right at the beginning of the 19th century four more were discovered: iridium, osmium, rhodium and palladium.

This was not the end. Fifteen years later, in 1844, after the death of Davy, Professor Klaus of the University of Kazan, in Russia, found still another element in the platinum-bearing ores. It was similar to platinum and he called it ruthenium. This brought the number of elements up to 57.

After this came a pause. No more new elements were discovered anywhere. It was during these years, the second quarter of the 19th century, that industry began to develop rapidly. The first railways were built in Europe and in America. The first steamboats appeared on the seas. And people began to go to the four corners of the earth in search of raw materials for industry; for ores, coal and other mineral deposits.

Tremendous collections of minerals and ores were made. Thousands of different substances passed through the hands of chemists, in factories and in laboratories, for accurate analysis. Yet no new elements were found in addition to the 57 already known.

Was it possible that all the elements that exist in the world had really been found and that it was useless to look for any more? No, those who were searching for the elements were not content.

They reasoned: We have, up to now, discovered only those elements which exist in large quantities and in many places on the earth and which are easily separated from other elements. But we know that all the known elements are very unevenly distributed over the earth. There is, for example, a good deal of iron in all parts of the world, much less copper, still less silver and very little gold. And there are, apparently, only a few tons of ruthenium in the whole world. Why not suppose that there are still rarer elements scattered about in minute quantities somewhere? We must investigate.

The search continued but it was fruitless. Ores from everywhere were examined: ores from Australia, from Greenland, from the neighbourhood of Paris and even from the volcano of Vesuvius. But all of them were composed of the elements already known. No one found any new elements.

Yet it was much easier to search for new substances than it had been in the time of Scheele and Lavoisier. The technique of chemical analysis improved with every passing year. Chemists could not only tell of what elements a given stone or clay was composed, they could tell, with great accuracy, how much of each element was present.

Experienced chemists could perform dozens of different operations and transformations with only a single gram of a substance. They made solutions of it, evaporated it, washed it, filtered it, heated it red hot, treated it with acids and with alkalis, burned it in fire and froze it on ice. They ground it in a mortar. And they were able to do all this without losing a single crumb of the substance!

Complicated analytical balances were invented, so sensitive that they could weigh a minute particle a thousand times lighter than a little one-gram weight. People learned to work in laboratories with unbelievable accuracy.

Yet no new elements were discovered.

Finally physics came to the aid of chemistry, just as once before the discoveries of the physicist Volta had helped the work of the chemist Davy. Then electricity had led to the discovery of many new elements. This time, half a century later, it was light that helped chemists to discover new elements.

Two friends, Robert Bunsen the chemist and Gustav Kirchhoff the physicist, combined their skills and succeeded in making the most remarkable discoveries.

2. Robert Bunsen and Gustav Kirchhoff

Robert Bunsen's life was as quiet and regular as the tick of a reliable old clock. He never knew poverty and need, he never strove for riches. He knew his science and nothing else.

He was not self-educated like Scheele and Davy. His parents saw to it that their son received a fine education and all the surroundings of his childhood and youth tended to make him interested in the study of science.

The German town of Göttingen, where he was born, was famed throughout the world for its university. The town lived off science, earned its daily bread by

Robert Bunsen
(1811 - 1899)

Gustav Kirchhoff
(1824 - 1887)

science, just as a port lives off the sea or a health resort off the sick.

Bunsen's father was a professor in the University of Göttingen, so no wonder the gifted son of an honoured professor also became a scientist in the course of time.

Robert finished the Gymnasium or High School, in 1828, at the age of seventeen. He immediately entered the university and three years later received the degree of Doctor of Science. Then he set out for a trip through Europe.

For a year and a half he jolted about in carriages or walked on foot from city to city, from country to country. He visited many factories - metal, chemical, and even sugar factories. He went down into coal mines and climbed snowy mountain peaks.

He made the acquaintance of the leading chemists of Germany, France, Switzerland and Austria. At Saint-Etienne in France, he saw for the first time what was in those days a fascinating novelty, railways, on which people travelled in carriages that were not pulled by horses.

The youthful doctor of science returned to his native Göttingen and settled down to the peaceful routine of a professional career. Pursuing the well-worn path that began with an appointment as privat-docent (professor's assistant) he started to teach chemistry.

This was in 1834. From that time on his entire life followed a regular pattern: lecture, laboratory, lectures again, and again laboratory.

At the age of twenty-five his daily programme was precisely what it was at fifty, and at fifty it was the same as it was at seventy. He got up at dawn, sat down at his desk to write out an account of his work and check over his results. Then he set out to deliver his lectures. From lecture room he went to the laboratory where he stayed until dinner time. After dinner he took a walk with some friend, then again returned to the laboratory.

True, there were a few occasions when he was obliged to interrupt this routine for a time. But it was not because of illness, for Bunsen was never ill in his life until he was a very old man. It was not love affairs, for he never fell in love; not family misfortunes, because he remained a bachelor; and not politics, for he kept out of politics and avoided public life. An occasional explosion or infection, the usual experience of every daring chemist, were the only accidents in his life.

Bunsen first gained recognition through his work on a complex chemical substance, cacodyl. It was while he was engaged in these first experiments that an explosion occurred in his laboratory as a result of which he lost one eye and was almost asphyxiated by the poisonous fumes.

Bunsen was a master of chemical analysis. He was constantly inventing clever, new methods of finding out the composition of different substances more accurately and quickly. Students and young chemists flocked to his laboratory from all over the world to learn his delicate technique.

Analysis, however, was not his only work. He made many important discoveries and invented many valuable pieces of laboratory apparatus.

But, as one of his friends used to say, Bunsen's greatest discovery was his 'discovery' of Gustav Kirchhoff.

Bunsen 'discovered', that is, met, Kirchhoff in 1851 in Breslau where he had been invited to work as professor of chemistry. They became friends at once. Kirchhoff lived much the same kind of well-regulated, peaceful, professorial life as Bunsen. He was as highly gifted too, but his speciality was physics and mathematics instead of chemistry.

When the two walked down the street together in Breslau, people would turn around to stare at the ill-matched pair.

In appearance they were totally unlike. When the two walked down the street together in Breslau, people would turn around to stare at the ill-matched pair. Imagine a big, broad-shouldered man with a cigar in his mouth and on his head a tall hat which towered so high it almost reached the level of the second storey windows. That was Bunsen. And beside him trotted a thin little man, making continual gestures with his hands. That was Kirchhoff.

Bunsen was no talker, while Kirchhoff loved to talk. When he was a little boy he chattered so incessantly his mother used to say to him sometimes:

"Keep still, Julchen! Do keep still a minute, Julchen!"

She called him 'Julia' because he was slender and delicate-looking, like a girl.

Kirchhoff was well versed in literature and loved to recite poetry. At one time he had been strongly tempted to become an actor. But this did not prevent his becoming deeply attached to Bunsen who knew nothing and wanted to know nothing but his science and who could not be enticed to leave his uncomfortable bachelor's quarters for any kind of social gathering.

A year and a half after they met, the two friends had to be separated. Bunsen was called to one of the oldest and best universities in Germany, the University of Heidelberg. He went; but he missed his friend Kirchhoff and Kirchhoff missed him so much that, finally, Bunsen succeeded in getting Kirchhoff invited to Heidelberg too. From that time on the two scientists were never again separated.

Almost every day they took long walks in the hilly country round Heidelberg, either alone or accompanied by one of their university colleagues. During these walks

Bunsen and Kirchhoff discussed the details of their respective experiments and scientific work. Before long the time came for them to join hands and work together on the same problem.

3. The colour of fire

In the year 1854 a gas factory was put up in Heidelberg and gas was piped to Bunsen's laboratory. They had to provide their own gas burners. Bunsen tried out several different kinds of burners but none of them was satisfactory. So he invented a wonderful new one.

Bunsen's burner did not smoke and could be regulated as desired. It could give a very hot, pure, colourless flame or a less hot but larger one. Or it could be turned down so as to give only the tiniest tongue of flame and yet not go out.

This amazingly simple and convenient burner is still used in all the laboratories of the world. It is called a Bunsen burner.

This amazingly simple and convenient burner is still used in all the laboratories of the world. It is called a Bunsen burner.

Bunsen loved to play with fire. He was a master hand at blowing chemical apparatus out of incandescent glass. Sometimes he sat at a table for hours, with a bellows in his hands, blowing the fire in a small soldering forge, while he skillfully manipulated a piece of glass in the fierce flame. He loved to blow the hot mass of glass into the most fantastic shapes. He fused metal on to the glass vessels, fused one tube to another and one utensil to another, holding the soft glass with his bare hands as if they were made of some heat-resisting steel, instead of skin and flesh like those of other people.

"You'll soon be smelling the roast meat!" the students used to say when the professor sat down to his blow torch.

And sometimes Bunsen's fingers actually began to smoke. But he would act as though it were nothing and never let go the hot glass. He had his own original way of cooling his fingers when the pain got too bad. He would put his hand up to his ear and pinch the lobe with the hot fingers. His 'fireproof' hands were famous all over the university.

When he was working at his glass blowing, Bunsen could not help noticing how the colour of the flame changed from time to time. He noticed it especially after he began using his own gas burner.

Generally it gave a hot, slightly bluish flame. But the moment a glass tube was held in this colourless flame it turned a yellowish hue. If the copper of the burner became red hot because the flame had gone inside the burner, the flame took on a greenish hue. If a bit of potassium salt was burned in it, it became rosy-lilac.

Bunsen experimented by putting bits of various substances on the end of a platinum wire and holding them in the flame and he found he could produce all sorts of gay-coloured lights with his colourless gas flame.

A bit of strontium salt gave a bright crimson flame.

Calcium - brick red

Barium - green

Sodium - bright yellow

And so on.

Bunsen knew that several chemists had been experimenting for some time trying to determine the composition of a substance by the colour of the flame. But they had not been very successful because they were working with an alcohol flame which has its own specific colour. In this colourless flame of a Bunsen burner everything showed up very clearly.

"This offers tremendous possibilities," thought Bunsen. "Think of being able to tell the composition of anything in just a few seconds!"

As a chemical analyst Bunsen well knew how much trouble it was to make an ordinary chemical analysis. One had to spend hours, sometimes even days, to determine the chemical composition of a given substance.

How simple it would be merely to hold a bit of the thing to be analysed in the flame of a Bunsen burner and see at once what it was made of!

However, it was not quite so simple as that.

It would be all right if your substance contained only potassium, for example, or only strontium and nothing else. Then the flame would have a pure, distinct lilac or crimson colour. But what if there were several different elements in the substance to be analysed, as is nearly always the case? Then it would be hard to get any definite indication even in the pure flame of a Bunsen burner. One colour would interfere with another.

Bunsen tried various devices in the hope of being able to see each colour separately. He looked at the flame through blue glass. With this he could sometimes distinguish in the flame the lilac colour of potassium and the red of lithium, although without the blue glass all he could see was the deep yellow colour of sodium. Yellow was not visible through the blue glass, so the lilac came out distinctly. But this was unreliable and would work in only about one case in a hundred.

Think of being able to tell the composition of anything in just a few seconds!

Once when he was out walking with Kirchhoff he was telling his friend about his difficulties and Kirchhoff remarked:

"As a physicist I should approach it in another way. In my opinion you should not look directly at the flame itself, but at its spectrum. Then all the colours would stand out much more distinctly."

Bunsen was delighted with this idea and the two decided to work together along this line and to begin immediately.

This conversation occurred early in the autumn of 1859. It had exceptionally important consequences for science. But before we tell about them we must first be sure we know what a spectrum is. To do that we must turn the pages back two hundred years.

4. Why Newton played with sunbeams

Back in the year 1660 the young scientist Isaac Newton, living in the peaceful town of Cambridge, used to spend days at a time doing the strangest thing - catching the reflections of sunbeams!

He sat for hours all alone in a dark room fussing at something, now and then muttering aloud to himself. Perhaps he was seeking an escape from the heat and was trying to keep cool in a darkened room? Hardly! He had carefully covered up every crack and the room was like a hot-house. He had a heavy wig on his head, in the fashion of his day, and the sweat was rolling down his face. Outside a fresh breeze was blowing.

Why was he sitting in this suffocating room?

He was catching the reflections of sunbeams on a piece of paper.

The shutters of all the windows were tightly closed so that no light could get in. In one of the shutters Newton had made a small, round hole about the size of your little finger. A narrow bar of sunlight came into the dark room through this little hole. Newton was walking quietly about the room, now holding his palm in the beam, now a sheet of paper, then letting the beam cross over to the opposite wall. A clear, bright reflection leapt from his hand to the wall, from the wall to the paper, from the paper to Newton's black doublet.

Was it possible that the young scientist could have been playing a childish game?

Newton was certainly not amusing himself. He was engaged in serious work. He was performing an experiment.

Isaac Newton
(1642 - 1727)

He had a triangular prism in his hand, just a piece of common glass with three equal facets. From time to time he held this little piece of glass in the beam of sunlight.

As soon as the glass cut the path of the sunbeam the round white circle of sunlight on the wall disappeared and in its place a long, many-coloured strip appeared.

"Where did the white light go?" Newton asked in bewilderment the first time he observed this inexplicable change.

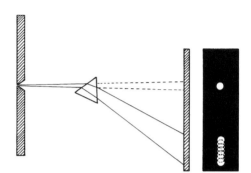

As soon as the glass cut the path of the sunbeam the round white circle of sunlight on the wall disappeared and in its place a long, many-coloured strip appeared.

He held the prism in one hand and with the other caught the sun's rays after they passed through the prism. He wriggled his finger, waved his hand. His fingers were bright red, yellow, green, blue and violet-coloured. He could not find the white light anywhere.

He repeated the experiment over and over. And every time the same thing happened: without the prism the sun rays were an ordinary white, but when they passed through the prism they came out painted all colours of the rainbow.

The moment he took the prism away the clear white spot of sunlight again danced on the wall, an exact copy of the hole in the shutter. But when he put the prism in the path of the rays, once more the elongated multi-coloured patch reappeared.

Newton called this coloured strip the spectrum.

The upper edge of the spectrum was always red. The red merged imperceptibly into orange, the orange into yellow, the yellow into green, the green into blue. At the very bottom of the spectrum came indigo and violet.

Newton racked his brain for a long time trying to discover where the spectrum came from. As soon as the sun showed itself in the morning he closed the shutters and began to catch the vari-coloured rays; and he remained in his self-imposed prison until evening, squinting in the light, the wonderful, coloured spectrum still dancing before his eyes.

He thought about it constantly, day and night, and finally he found the answer.

The light by the sun is not really white, he concluded. It only looks white to us. In reality a shower of brilliant, multi-coloured rays is pouring down from the sky and when the rays are all together our eyes cannot distinguish one from another. Therefore the sun's light appears to be white. But when these mingled rays pass through a prism, the prism scatters them and we see each one by itself.

Each ray makes a small round spot of light, the exact copy of the hole in the shutter. The red one is at the top because the red rays are least refracted by the prism. The violet ones are at the bottom because the prism refracts them most of all.

The others are distributed between the red and the violet.

The edge of each one of these little circles overlaps the edge of the next one, and so, in place of the round white copy of the hole in the shutter, we get on the wall an extended multi-coloured strip - the spectrum.

Newton's explanation must have seemed very strange at first. It was difficult to grasp the idea that white light is really not white at all; that the sun shining down from the sky overhead is not a brilliant white sun, but a wonderful, multi-coloured one which is at one and the same time red and yellow and green and violet.

But this unbelievable statement is nevertheless true. Remember how transparent dewdrops and raindrops gleam with brilliant colours in the sunlight!

Newton carried out scores of experiments in his darkened room before he reached the conclusion that the white light of the sun is really a mixture of rays. And his proofs were so convincing that it was hard to dispute him. He not only split up the white, mixed light into its component colours, he also reversed the operation and, passing the coloured rays through another prism, showed that by recombining they came out white again.

He devised the following experiment too: he painted all the colours of the sun's rays on a circular piece of wood, then whirled it rapidly on its axis. The whirling wheel appeared to be white, when as a matter of fact it was all striped with colour and there was not a single speck of white on it.

Remember how transparent dewdrops gleam with brilliant colours in the sunlight!

5. Fraunhofer's lines

But after all, what does the sun have to do with it? We were talking about the flame of the Bunsen burner and the analysis of chemical substances. Why did we suddenly begin to talk about the sun and its spectrum?

You will find out right away.

What did Newton do? He discovered, in his dark room, that the sun's light is not of a single colour. Instead it consists of rays of the different colours and these rays are scattered away from their straight path by a prism.

Now, is all other light, artificial light as well as the light of the sun, also not uniform in colour? For example, the flame of a spirit lamp or of a candle: does it also consist of rays of different colours?

Yes, artificial light may also be split up into different colours.

In 1814, a clever German optician, Fraunhofer, was studying the spectra of different kinds of lamps, trying to find a source of light that would give only rays of one colour. He needed such light for testing the quality of high-grade magnifying glass which he was preparing for some optical instruments.

Fraunhofer did not succeed in finding a single-coloured light but he did make some very curious discoveries.

He also worked in a dark room like Newton but he admitted the light through a very narrow slit in a window or door instead of through a round hole. He placed the lamp outside, directly in front of the opening and put a telescope behind the prism and caught the spectrum in it.

The telescope had a high magnifying power and the prism was made of a special kind of glass which very strongly scattered the rays. He therefore got an extremely long, bright, sharp spectrum.

First Fraunhofer placed an oil lamp at the slit. When he looked through his telescope he noticed that two very bright yellow lines stood out side by side in the many-hued ribbon of light and that these lines were just the width of the slit. He turned the lens of the telescope and looked again. The yellow lines were still there. He realised what this meant: that of all the rays coming from the lamp there were two so especially bright that they did not run into the others but gave sharp, separate images of the slit.

When he used an alcohol lamp instead of an oil one he found that the yellow lines again appeared in the field of vision of the telescope.

Next Fraunhofer tried a candle.

Next he tried a candle - again the yellow lines stood out. And they were always in the same position, provided the prism and the telescope were not moved and the long spectrum remained unchanged.

Then he looked for the yellow lines in the sun's spectrum. But they were not there. However, he did notice something else: the whole long brilliant, multi-coloured band of the sun's spectrum was intersected by a number of dark lines. He counted more than 500 of them. Each one of these narrow dark lines, the width of the slit, always occupied exactly the same position. Some were lighter, some darker, but others stood out clearly and appeared jet black against the bright background of the spectrum. Fraunhofer gave the names A, B, C, D, etc., to these especially clear-cut black lines.

"How remarkable!" he thought, as he looked at the black lines. "It looks as though certain colours are lacking in the sun's light."

He began to examine the lines more carefully and was more astonished than ever to notice that there was a deep black double line in the very same position where the bright yellow lines had appeared in the spectrum of the candle and the lamp.

During the day he would let the sun shine through the slit - and always there were those black lines in the spectrum in precisely the same position.

In the evening he would place a lamp or candle at the slit and there would appear in the very same place in the spectrum a bright double yellow line. And both pairs coincided exactly.

That is , the rays which shone most brightly in the artificial light were just the ones that were missing in the light of the sun.

A strange, inexplicable phenomenon!

Many other scientists studied the spectra of different sources of light - of stearine candles, electric sparks, voltaic arcs. In nearly all cases they found the bright yellow lines and frequently they found other bright lines too.

In the sun's spectrum they kept finding more and more dark lines, 'Fraunhofer's lines,' as they began to call them. However, no one was able to give a satisfactory explanation of what caused them. Some scientists were very close to the right answer but were still not able to clear up the whole mystery.

It remained for Kirchhoff and Bunsen to do this.

6. Spectral analysis

The two friends began by constructing a spectroscope, an instrument for observing spectra.

One fine day Kirchhoff turned up at the laboratory with a cigar box and two telescopes that had seen their best days. With these simple materials they made themselves a spectroscope.

The light was admitted through a telescope with the eye-piece replaced by a slit. Such a tube with a slit in it is called a collimator. It is easy to see that the collimator served the same purpose as the shutter with an opening in it which Newton had in his darkened room.

The rays from the collimator fell on a prism inside the cigar box. Kirchhoff had pasted black paper all over the inside of the cigar box so that no light could possibly get in.

The prism refracted the rays coming in through the slit. A spectrum was produced.

Kirchhoff turned up at the laboratory with a cigar box and two telescopes that had seen their best days. With these simple materials they made themselves a spectroscope.

Bunsen and Kirchhoff looked at it through the other telescope, just as Fraunhofer had done.

Naturally Kirchhoff, being a physicist, did most of the work in the making of the spectroscope. But Bunsen was not idle in the meantime.

He was preparing substances of great purity to be examined in the flame. He dissolved many different salts, secured crystals from the solutions, filtered them, washed them, made more solutions, etc., until he obtained unusually good specimens.

True, this was painstaking and uninteresting drudgery at times. But from his youth Bunsen had learned patience and perseverance in his scientific work. Both friends were accurate and intelligent workers. And so they got results.

To test the instrument, Kirchhoff, using a mirror as a reflector, first admitted a bright beam of sunlight through the slit. He looked in and was delighted to see a fine, multi-coloured spectrum, all intersected with black Fraunhofer lines.

Next he closed the window shutters and put a lighted Bunsen burner at the slit. This time it was dark in the collimator and Kirchhoff could distinguish only the dimmest illumination as he looked in through the tube. The Bunsen burner was right up close to the slit in the collimator and was burning with a hot flame, hotter than molten steel. Yet the light of the flame produced hardly any spectrum at all, it was so white and colourless.

The picture changed sharply when Bunsen began to put bits of different materials into it. First he took pure table salt, which chemists call sodium chloride because it is composed of sodium and chlorine. Bunsen put a small pinch of this salt on a platinum wire and held it in the flame. The flame immediately turned bright yellow. Kirchhoff put his eye to the telescope.

"I see two yellow lines side by side," he said. "Nothing more. Just a dark background and on it two yellow lines."

They got exactly the same yellow lines from other compounds of sodium. Bunsen tried one after another: sodium carbonate, sodium nitrate, also called saltpetre, and many other sodium salts. They all gave exactly the same spectrum: two yellow lines on a dark background and always in the same position.

Everything was perfectly clear now: the sodium salt had instantly split up as a result of the heat, the sodium had changed into hot vapours and it was these vapours that gave the invariable yellow light.

As soon as the sodium salt was all gone the flame again became colourless.

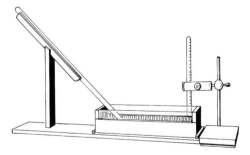

Bunsen's gas analysis apparatus.

Washing the platinum wire thoroughly, Bunsen next put a tiny pinch of potassium salt on it and held it in the flame.

The flame became a delicate lilac colour. Kirchhoff took his place at the tube.

Silence for a few seconds.

"What do you see, Gustav?" Bunsen asked.

"I see one violet line and one red line on a dark background and between them an almost complete spectrum without distinct bright lines."

All salts of lithium gave one bright red line and a less vivid orange one. The spectrum of strontium had one bright blue line and several dark red ones.

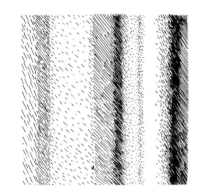

The hot vapours of each element gave out rays of a distinct colour, and the prism directed these rays to a specific place in the spectrum.

So with every element. The hot vapours of every one of them, it proved, gave out rays of a distinct colour and the prism directed these rays to a specific place in the spectrum.

Robert and Gustav were enchanted at the sight of these beautiful coloured lines in the spectroscope. Bunsen made a special little stand for the platinum wire so that he would not have to sit there and hold it all the time but could also look into the spectroscope.

Spots were beginning to dance before their eyes, but Kirchhoff did not want to stop.

"We must make a drawing of it all," he said. "We must have all the spectra on paper so as to make comparisons with them later."

"Wait a minute," said Bunsen stopping him. "We don't know the most important thing of all - what kind of spectrum we'll get if we mix several different salts together and hold them in the flame - for instance sodium, potassium and lithium."

So they decided to try this experiment and then declare a recess. They were both impatient to find out whether they could determine by the spectroscope the composition of substances which contained many different elements.

The crucial moment had arrived. Kirchhoff paced back and forth rubbing his tired eyes. Bunsen, unperturbed as usual, spent a long time carefully mixing several salts. Finally he put a few particles of the mixture on the wire and held it in the flame. The flame immediately became bright yellow - that meant the sodium predominated over the other colours.

And the spectroscope, what did it show?

Kirchhoff looked into the tube for a long time. The room was very still. The salts crackled in the flame. Bunsen's hand, holding one end of the wire, trembled slightly.

"I can tell you what salts you mixed together," Kirchhoff said at last. "You mixed sodium, potassium, lithium and strontium."

"Correct!" cried Bunsen. He fastened the wire in its holder and ran to the tube of the spectroscope. This is what he saw:

Each bright line stood out separately, each in its place. The two yellow lines of sodium stood out the clearest. But the violet line of potassium, the red line of lithium, and the deep blue of strontium all came out distinctly in the different parts of the broad, many-coloured strip of the spectrum.

Just as a person may be picked out in a crowd by the sound of his voice, so every element in the mixture could be identified by the coloured ray which its flaming vapours gave out. The prism distributed to its own position on the spectrum the rays sent out by each different element so that no colour could conceal another.

Kirchhoff and Bunsen could congratulate themselves. The goal they had set themselves was reached: they had discovered a new way of making chemical analysis - spectral analysis.

7. Looking for something in the daytime with a lantern

Days passed. A mild golden autumn bedecked the gardens of Heidelberg. The wooded hills around the town were bright with all the colours of the red-yellow portion of the spectrum. The air was clear, pure, crisp. But Bunsen and Kirchhoff could no longer indulge in their walks. They sat in the laboratory and worked - worked feverishly, intently.

They had a magical instrument in their hands. It disclosed the secrets of the world as easily and simply as in a fairy tale and the two friends never tired of working with it, rejoicing in one discovery after another.

The spectroscope turned out to be so delicate and sensitive an apparatus that even the most elaborate and accurate scales, which could weigh a grain of sand, seemed crude and clumsy in comparison.

How much sodium would you guess has to be present in the flame of a Bunsen burner in order to be able to observe the double yellow lines in the spectroscope?

You would probably guess a gram, or half a gram, or one-thousandth part of a gram, that is, a milligram.

$$\frac{1}{3,000,000,000} \text{ gm}$$

You would be wrong. A particle of soda or sodium salt weighing three million times less than a milligram is enough to make the flame send the yellow rays into the spectroscope!

Can you imagine how little one three-millionth of a milligram is? If you were to dissolve in a glass of water a pinch of ordinary salt weighing one gram, then pour this into a barrel holding four pails of pure water, then dip a glass of water out of this barrel and pour it into a barrel holding forty pails, finally in one drop of water from the last barrel there would be about one three-millionth of a milligram of sodium salt.

Yet such an incredibly small amount of sodium as that can be discovered by means of the spectroscope.

Is it any wonder that Fraunhofer and the scientists who came after him found the yellow line in the spectrum of every lamp and candle they examined? It was sodium that gave the yellow line. Several millionths of a milligram of ordinary salt can doubtless be found in any lamp wick or in candle wax - or as a matter of fact in anything.

No matter how pure the air in the laboratory may seem, there are still many ways in which sodium can get into the flame. If Bunsen, for example, happened to touch the end of the platinum wire with his finger for just a second it would leave a trace of salt on it. Sweat constantly passes out through the pores of the skin and sweat is salty. If, after touching the wire with his finger, Bunsen were to put the wire in the flame the yellow line would appear in the spectrum.

When a dusty book is slammed shut near a lighted Bunsen burner, there are immediately yellow sparks in the colourless flame and the spectroscope dutifully records with its yellow line the presence of sodium salt.

Where does the sodium in the book come from? From the ocean. Winds blowing in from the sea pick up the tiny, microscopic spray of salt sea water and carry invisible particles of sodium salt for thousands of miles inland. These minute particles dance about in the dust and settle down to earth with it. Blow dust into the flame of a Bunsen burner and the spectroscope immediately announces: "Sodium!"

Bunsen and Kirchhoff discovered that we live in a very dirty world. They found that dirt appears on almost everything, often when it seems impossible for it to be present.

Always the faithful spectroscope would expose these supposedly clean substances and would announce:

"There are impurities present. Maybe there is only the most minute quantity, maybe only the thousandth or millionth part of a gram or even less, but impurities there are."

As a police dog picking up the scent tracks down a fleeing criminal, so the spectroscope disclosed the existence of tiny particles of substances in the most unexpected places. The bright lines of the spectrum seemed to say to the two scientists: "Look, here is sodium and there are potassium, strontium, barium, magnesium and many other elements that you least expected to find."

One morning when Kirchhoff arrived at the laboratory Bunsen astonished him by announcing:

"Do you know where I found lithium? In tobacco ashes!"

Hitherto lithium, a very light metal, related to sodium and potassium, had been considered one of the rarest elements in the world. It was found in only three or four rare minerals. And here, suddenly, lithium was discovered in ordinary tobacco! The spectroscope had tracked it down.

And not in tobacco alone. Hardly a day passed that Bunsen and Kirchhoff did not discover this element in some new place.

Lithium was found in ordinary granite, in the salt water of the Atlantic, in fresh river water and in the pure water of mountain streams. There was lithium everywhere: in tea, in milk, in grapes, in human blood and in the tissues of animals. Even in meteorites which came to the earth from cosmic space, even there, lithium was found.

Armed with the spectroscope Bunsen and Kirchhoff spent weeks hunting for elements. At first it was a continual delight to them to find a hidden store of elements in every stone or chemical specimen. But this amusement soon began to lose its charm. They wanted more. They began to dream about the discovery of new elements, never before seen by the human eye.

It was not unreasonable to hope they might now be able to find elements which had always before slipped unnoticed through chemists' hands because they were present only in such small quantities. But the spectroscope ferreted out things even when there was merely a millionth or a billionth of a gram of them present. Why, then, was it not reasonable to suppose that their new instrument would put Bunsen and Kirchhoff on the track of unknown elements?

Bunsen, aided by Kirchhoff, searched for new elements.

And a very important part in this search was played by those dark lines of the sun's spectrum - the Fraunhofer lines.

"Do you know where I found lithium? In tobacco ashes!"

8. Sunlight and Drummond light

One day Kirchhoff said to his friend:

"Do you know what I keep thinking about all the time, Robert?"

"About new elements," Bunsen interrupted.

"No, believe it or not, that isn't it. I keep thinking about Fraunhofer lines. What can they mean? Why is the sun's spectrum striped with all those dark lines? We've been able to explain many things but we haven't yet found any explanation for the lines."

"That's so. But as far as I am concerned, I'm more interested in new elements at present."

"But just think a moment, Robert, why is it that the yellow sodium line is always in the very same place as the black 'D' line in the sun's spectrum? I'm convinced that does not happen by accident. There must be some connection between these two facts."

The next clear day, Kirchhoff spent studying the sun's spectrum. Some time previously he had added to the spectroscope a scale with divisions marked on it. Now every line of the spectrum always appeared above a special number on the scale so that it was impossible to confuse one line with another.

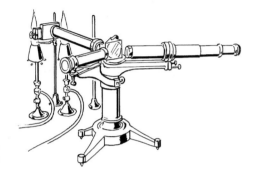

Kirchhoff's improved spectroscope

The sun's rays shone straight into the slit in the collimator. A big, glowing, solid spectrum spread out beyond the prism. There was not a single bright line in it. The wide bands of colour merged into one another and only the dark Fraunhofer lines stood out against the light background, like the palings of a picket fence. Kirchhoff found the number on the scale which corresponded to the yellow line of sodium. That line, of course, did not appear in the sun's spectrum but in its place, directly above the number on the scale, was a heavy dark line - the double 'D' line.

Next Kirchhoff shut out the sunlight, placed a burner in front of the slit and put a little sodium salt into the flame. Now, in place of the magnificent, many-hued spectrum of the sun, he could see only two lonely yellow bars.

This suggested an interesting idea to him.

"I'll let the sun's rays in again," he thought, "leaving the burner right where it is. We will see how one spectrum fits over the other."

To prevent the brilliant spectrum of the sun from completely eclipsing the sodium flame he passed the sun's rays through several layers of ground glass. The soft weak light of the sun then shone through the flame of the burner and from there entered the slit, along with the rays of incandescent sodium.

And what did the spectroscope show?

The regular solar spectrum, though dimmer than usual, appeared. But it had one peculiarity: the sodium line was shining brightly in the place where the Fraunhofer 'D' line belonged. One spectrum was superimposed on the other.

Kirchhoff increased the strength of the sunshine a little; the sodium line remained in the same place. Then he let the sun's rays shine full force right through the sodium flame into the slit.

When he looked into the spectroscope now he grunted in surprise. Contrary to his expectation, the bright sodium line had disappeared. In its place was a thick black line. Although the flame was still burning brightly, and just as before emitting a great stream of yellow rays, there was a black, empty space where the yellow line had previously been.

Kirchhoff was astounded.

Most amazing of all was the fact that the dark 'D' line now appeared a good deal more distinctly than before. It was much darker and stood out much more sharply than the other Fraunhofer lines, despite the fact that intense rays from the incandescent sodium, scattered by the prism of the spectroscope, were directed to the exact spot where those black lines were.

It would not have astonished Kirchhoff had the yellow sodium line appeared paler than usual against the background of the brilliant solar spectrum. Naturally the flame of the burner was far less intense than the sun's rays. But the disappearance of this sodium line and the appearance in its place of an unusually black 'D' line, produced a real puzzle.

Kirchhoff left the spectroscope and stood gazing thoughtfully out of the window. His brain was grappling with a serious problem.

"It looks as though I have hit upon a clue to the solution of something," he said to himself.

Bunsen was not in the laboratory at the time, so Kirchhoff called an assistant and asked him to put in front of the spectroscope what is known as a 'Drummond light', named after the Englishman who invented it.

A Drummond light is a light made by burning together two gases, hydrogen and oxygen, fed from two tubes simultaneously. The hydrogen burns fiercely in the oxygen and this hot flame is directed on to a rod made of pure lime. The lime gets white hot and gives out a blinding light.

The incandescent light does not give separated bright lines, as the luminous

Kirchhoff was astounded.

vapours do, but gives a solid, continuous, even spectrum without lines of any kind, similar to the spectrum of the sun, except that there are no dark lines in it.

Why did Kirchhoff want a Drummond light? He wanted to use it as an artificial sun.

His idea was to pass the rays of the Drummond light through the sodium flame into the spectroscope. He was anxious to see whether or not the yellow sodium lines would behave in the same way against the background of the continuous spectrum of a Drummond light as against the spectrum of the sun.

Kirchhoff first tried passing the Drummond light alone through the slit, without the yellow sodium flame. He observed in the spectroscope a pure continuous spectrum without a sign of either a dark or a coloured line.

Then he placed the salt in the burner and moved the flame close up under the slit so that its rays would cut right through those of the Drummond light.

Instantly the dark twin 'D' line appeared in the yellow part of the spectrum of the Drummond light.

Instantly the dark twin 'D' line appeared in the yellow part of the spectrum of the Drummond light.

"An artificial Fraunhofer line!" Kirchhoff whispered to himself. "That's just what it is! Now I think I am beginning to get to the bottom of the thing. The dark lines are the result of the light's passing through another illuminating substance - through incandescent vapours. Evidently the sodium flame not only sends out yellow rays; it also absorbs other yellow rays, rays of the same colour but coming from some other source of light. True, yellow rays from the burner itself still fall on this spot. But they are weak, in comparison with the powerful Drummond light. Therefore the dark gap appears colourless in the bright spectrum of the Drummond light or of sunlight."

Bunsen came into the laboratory to find his friend in a state of great excitement. Talking rapidly, nervously, and often repeating himself, Kirchhoff tried to tell Bunsen about his discovery.

He went over all his experiments one after the other to show Bunsen the origin of the Fraunhofer lines.

"I can make them myself!" he exclaimed. "Now you can produce Fraunhofer lines in your laboratory yourself, any time you want to. Think of that!"

9. Chemistry of the Sun

It took Kirchhoff a long time to get to sleep that night. He kept thinking and thinking, and the more he thought the more excited he became, and the less he felt like sleeping.

"I mean that our spectral analysis may be used not only to investigate substances on the earth but also to study the composition of the sun and the stars."

Next morning, pale and hollow-eyed, he went to see Bunsen as soon as he had finished his lectures. Without waiting to say good morning, he burst out:

"I've been thinking about what we discovered yesterday, Robert, and it has led me to some most remarkable conclusions - so daring I can hardly believe them myself."

"Really? And what are they?"

"There is sodium in the sun!"

"Sodium in the sun! Why, what do you mean by that?"

"I mean that our spectral analysis may be used not only to investigate substances on the earth but also to study the composition of the sun and the stars. We can recognise the elements on the earth by the bright lines of their spectra. But we can tell what elements there are in the sun by the dark Fraunhofer lines."

This was surely a bold stroke of genius - to find a way to analyse the sun and the stars just as you do a simple mineral or piece of clay.

Kirchhoff reasoned as follows:

The sun consists of a compact, super-heated core surrounded by a rarefied atmosphere of incandescent gases. The light which comes from the sun to the earth comes from the surface of the compact core. This light contains rays of all colours, thousands of shades. If it came directly to us, if it did not have to pass first through the sun's incandescent atmosphere, all these rays would reach the earth and the sun's spectrum would be pure and continuous, like the spectrum of a Drummond light.

But the sunlight must first pass through the incandescent gases of the sun's atmosphere. These gases also give off light, though much less intense than that of the sun's core. Therefore, the atmosphere acts just like the sodium flame in Kirchhoff's experiment: it absorbs, intercepts, part of the sun's rays.

What rays does it hold back? Those very rays which are sent out by the elements composing the sun's atmosphere.

So, when the light emerges from the sun's atmosphere and proceeds on to the earth, many of its rays are lacking. And when it passes into a spectroscope this light does not give a complete, coloured spectrum but a coloured band, intersected by dark Fraunhofer lines.

The dark 'D' line appears in the place where the yellow bright line of sodium would ordinarily be. That indicates, Kirchhoff believed, the presence of incandescent vapours of sodium in the sun's atmosphere.

But perhaps the coincidence of the black line 'D' with the yellow one of sodium was merely accidental?

Suppose it is so, then the experiment with the Drummond light proves there is nothing coincidental about it. But if this is true, how explain the coincidence of the lines of iron?

Kirchhoff and Bunsen produced, by means of an electric current, some glowing incandescent iron vapours and recorded their spectrum. They counted 60 distinct bright lines in it. They compared this spectrum with that of the sun and this is what they discovered:

Every bright line in the spectrum of iron corresponded in position to a dark line of the same width and sharpness in the spectrum of the sun.

There was no possibility that the coincidence of these 60 lines could all be accidental.

It was inevitable that these lines should coincide because iron, in the form of incandescent vapours, exists in the sun's atmosphere and these vapours hold back all the rays ordinarily sent out by vapours of incandescent iron.

By the same method Kirchhoff discovered about 30 more elements in the sun: copper, lead, tin, hydrogen, potassium and many other substances which are found on the earth.

These two scientific friends were looking for an easy way of analysing chemical substances on the earth and they found a way of analysing the sun!

Kirchhoff sent the first announcement of his discovery to the Berlin Academy of Science on the 20th October, 1859. He followed this announcement almost immediately with another, telling how he had, by means of mathematical calculations, proved that incandescent gas must absorb rays identical with those it sent out. So Kirchhoff used theory to corroborate practice.

All this time he kept working steadily at further experiments and investigations. All of them confirmed the deductions he had already made: that the sun contains common substances such as are found on the earth.

The news of this discovery flew round the world.

The names of Kirchhoff and Bunsen were on the lips of every educated person.

Just think of it! These scientists, sitting in their laboratory on the earth, were able to discover the composition of a heavenly body millions of miles distant from us!

So the sun, and soon after it, the stars, lost much of their mystery for man.

10. Caesium and rubidium

In May, 1860, the regular mail bag addressed to the Berlin Academy of Science was forwarded from the Heidelberg post office. This time it was Bunsen, instead of Kirchhoff, reporting.

While Kirchhoff was devoting all his time to studying the atmosphere of the sun, his friend had not forgotten about earthly affairs. Bunsen kept up his search for new elements.

He tested hundreds of specimens in the flame of a gas burner or the discharge of an electric spark: Minerals, ores, salts, waters, vegetable ashes, the tissues of animals. And the spectroscope monotonously announced to him a dozen times a day: "There is potassium, calcium, sodium, barium, lithium..."

By this time Bunsen was as familiar with the coloured lines of every one of their spectra as he was with the five fingers of his own hands, or the view from his bedroom window. Without even glancing at the scale, he could recognise any of them instantly by their position on the spectrum, by their colour and intensity. He could shut his eyes and see in his mind's eye the spectrum of any element as distinctly as if drawn on a blackboard. He dreamed at night of yellow, red, blue, violet lines against a coloured dark background.

Then lo and behold one day he discovered new, unfamiliar lines among them!

It was when he was analysing the mineral water of the Durkheim springs. This was an ordinary mineral water - salty and somewhat bitter to the taste. Doctors prescribed it for the treatment of various diseases. Bunsen happened to have some of it quite by accident and was examining it along with a number of other specimens he was testing at that time.

At first the spectroscope did not announce anything unusual: merely sodium, potassium, lithium, calcium, strontium.

But Bunsen had the delicate intuition of the analyst.

"There's a large quantity of all these substances in Durkheim water," he reasoned, "and for that reason these lines are too bright. Furthermore, calcium and strontium give many different lines and if there happened to be an infinitesimal amount of some unknown element in this drop, it might be impossible to distinguish it. I must get the calcium, strontium and lithium out of the way."

He did this, leaving only the sodium and potassium, and a small quantity of lithium salts.

Then he tried a drop in the flame and looked into the spectroscope. His heart

The water from Durkheim springs was an ordinary mineral water - salty and somewhat bitter to the taste.

skipped a beat. Modestly hidden away among the familiar lines of sodium, potassium and lithium were two unfamiliar little bright blue threads.

Bunsen, to make sure he had not made a mistake, scanned the coloured charts of the spectra which he and Kirchhoff had drawn. No, there was not a single element that had those two blue lines in that place. Strontium had a blue line, but only one. And there were two distinct lines here and none of the rest of the spectrum of strontium was visible.

Was it a new element?

Bunsen put drop after drop into the flame. The blue lines continued to appear steadily in their place.

As he looked at them Bunsen suddenly recalled a story about Columbus which he had read long ago in his childhood. How in the year 1492 the adventurous admiral had set sail in an old leaky caravel on an uncharted sea. How for thirty-three days the sailors saw only sky and water, water and sky. How they sailed on and on, hope giving way to fear and disappointment and then hope flaring up again. At last one night, in the shoreless wastes of the ocean, Columbus suddenly saw, away off in the west, a dim little twinkle of light.

Who could say what treasures lay hidden behind that glimmer of light on an unknown shore?

And who could say what unknown thing signalling with bright, sky-blue rays was hidden in the drop of Durkheim water?

Bunsen, the Heidelberg chemist, did not weep as Columbus wept when he discovered the new land. Naturally there were no tears in his eyes when he saw the signal of an unknown substance in the spectroscope. Nevertheless, he too, felt at that moment the keen joy of the explorer who stands on the threshold of a long-looked-for discovery.

Bunsen named the new element caesium, which in Latin means 'sky-blue.'

He was on the right path. What he had to do now was to follow this trail till it led him to the blue substance itself.

He had to separate caesium out from the other substances so that when he had it in a pure form he could see what it was.

And this was no easy thing to do! There was only the faintest trace of the new element in the Durkheim water - one forty-thousandth of a gram in a whole glass. If Bunsen were to try to get even ten or twenty grams of it in his laboratory vessels he would have to sit there and fuss with Durkheim water all the rest of his life, boiling it and treating it with chemical reagents.

He set about the work in another way.

There was a chemical factory near Heidelberg where soda was manufactured. The factory had huge vats and furnaces and mechanical pumps. Bunsen made arrangements with the manager of the plant to spend several weeks evaporating and chemically treating about 12,000 gallons of mineral water.

From this sea of liquid he got in all seven grams of pure caesium salt. But, in addition, he found another new element!

This is the way it happened: Bunsen was creeping up on the caesium step by step, eliminating the other elements from the water, one, two, three at a time. Finally there were only two salts left - caesium and potassium. While the potassium was being washed out little by little, the spectroscope gave an unexpected signal: two new violet lines followed by some green, yellow and especially vivid dark red ones.

There was another new element lurking in the Durkheim water!

That made 59 elements. Bunsen named this last element rubidium, the Latin word for 'dark red.' From the quantity of Durkheim water he was testing Bunsen obtained a little more of this newest element than of Caesium - ten grams in all.

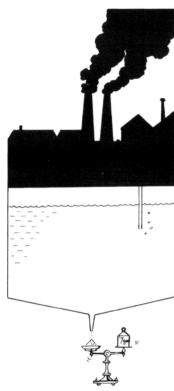

Bunsen made arrangements with the manager of the plant to spend several weeks evaporating and chemically treating about 12,000 gallons of mineral water.

11. More 'boisterous' metals

Seven grams and ten grams - not a very large supply, but ample for a master chemist like Bunsen.

He tried various combinations of caesium and rubidium with the old elements and observed how these new compounds acted. He learned how they tasted, how readily they would dissolve in water, what size crystals they formed, at what temperatures they melted - and many other things besides.

Caesium and rubidium turned out to be very like Davy's famous boisterous metals, potassium and sodium and their triplet, lithium.

Both caesium and rubidium proved to be light, silvery metals, though slightly heavier than lithium. They were soft like wax, even softer than potassium and sodium. They took fire when exposed to air and turned into caustic alkali. They ran about on top of water, flaming and crackling, and they were even more unstable than potassium and sodium. Also like Davy's metals, they could be kept only in kerosene.

Chlorine salts of caesium and rubidium looked exactly like common cooking salt, which chemists call sodium chloride. From their appearance the most experienced cook would never hesitate to salt the soup with them.

Nitric acid salts of caesium and rubidium proved to be similar to saltpetre which chemists call potassium nitrate. Gunpowder could also be made of these nitric acid salts of caesium and rubidium.

Caustic caesium alkali (caesium hydroxide) and caustic rubidium alkali (rubidium hydroxide) were slippery to the touch and had a soapy taste like caustic potash and caustic soda. The most experienced soap maker could not have told them apart and would have made soap of them with a clear conscience. He would have got a pretty good soap too. But a small cake of it might have cost as much as twenty pounds.

12. Getting ahead of our story

Maybe some reader has been thinking for a long time: "All this is very fine - Kirchhoff and Bunsen performed wonderful experiments. They were the inventors of spectral analysis. They found out what the sun is made of. They discovered two rare elements, compounds of which could be used to make soap and gunpowder, if they were not dearer than gold. But of what practical use were these discoveries? Did they help to advance technology or industry in any way?"

Yes, they did, although not right away. Great scientific discoveries are not always of practical use at once. But in the end they do inevitably have practical uses, sometimes where least expected.

When Bunsen discovered the rare metal, caesium, in Durkheim water, he never dreamed that the new element would some day be used in television. He could not have known, for at that time there were no such things as television cameras. There was not even any radio telegraphy. But caesium is used today in the photo-electric cells that are a part of all television cameras.

When Kirchhoff and Bunsen directed the rays of the sun or of a gas flame into their spectroscope, they had no idea that the fruits of their work would some day be used in airships. They could not have had any such idea because airships had not yet been invented. But a few decades later airship pilots made very good use indeed of the results of the work of the Heidelberg scientists. You will hear about that in a later chapter.

Neither did Kirchhoff and Bunsen know that, thanks to their spectroscope, people would some day learn to make long-lived electric lamps. In 1859 there were no

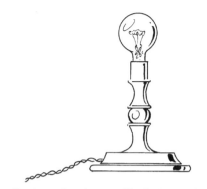

But later, thanks specifically to spectral analysis, people learned to prolong the life of electric lamps.

electric lamps of any kind, either long-lived or short-lived. But later, thanks specifically to spectral analysis, people learned to prolong the life of electric lamps. You may wonder how this happened. Well, this is another thing you will find out later on in our story.

Bunsen's and Kirchhoff's discoveries aided industry and technology in many, many ways. We cannot tell you about all of them in this book. There are too many.

13. A sun element

Bunsen and Kirchhoff soon had lots of imitators. Chemists everywhere were excited when they heard about the discovery of the new elements. One scientific laboratory after another installed the new apparatus which worked equally well on the sun or on a drop of water. Every imaginable substance was heated up and examined in the spectroscope in the search for new lines.

And they found them, too!

In 1861 the Englishman Crookes obtained from a chemical plant a particular kind of clay which settled to the bottom in the lead vessels where sulphuric acid was being manufactured. Crookes discovered an unknown green line in the spectrum of this clay. This led to the discovery of a new element, thallium, a heavy metal.

Two years later the German chemists, Richter and Reich, observed a new line of an indigo colour in the spectrum of a zinc ore. They named this new element indium. Indium also proved to be a metal, a white one.

Five years later scientists again came on the track of an unfamiliar element. But this time it was astronomers instead of chemists. And the new line was found in the spectrum of the sun.

It was during a solar eclipse. A French astronomer, Janssen, and an English astronomer, Lockyer, directed the tube of the spectroscope toward the sun and discovered in the resulting spectrum a bright yellow line next to the place usually occupied by the yellow line of sodium.

During an eclipse the moon covers the bright disc of the sun. Only the upper layers of its incandescent atmosphere extend beyond the dark shadow of the moon and send their weak rays unobstructed to the earth. It was in the spectrum of this light, which is quite unlike the ordinary solar spectrum with its dark Fraunhofer lines, that Janssen discovered the new yellow line.

What element was it that was emitting those yellow rays?

A girl with helium filled balloons.

Who could say? You cannot put the sun in a chemical flask, and you cannot evaporate it in a factory vat.

All the scientists could say about Janssen's discovery was that there was an unfamiliar element in the sun which had never been found on the earth. They named this new element helium. (Helios is the Greek word for sun.)

They called it helium, but there was no way of finding out what it was, how it looked and what its properties were.

It would be interesting, wouldn't it, to solve the riddle of this sun substance - to find out whether or not it resembles elements found on earth or whether it is some entirely different kind of material? Must we wait for the answer until people learn to fly to the sun in rockets? How can we find out?

Perhaps the secret of helium will be revealed to you much sooner than you think - even before you finish reading this book.

Meanwhile, listen to the story of how a Russian chemist, Dmitri Mendeleev, discovered several new elements in his office, while sitting at his desk.

He had never seen these elements either with the naked eye or by means of the spectroscope. He discovered them entirely through application of his great powers of reasoning.

CHAPTER 4
The Law of Mendeleev

1. A chemical maze

In 1867 Dmitri Mendeleev, a young chemist, was invited to fill the vacant chair of General Chemistry at the University of St. Petersburg.

It was a great honour to be asked to give the most important course in chemistry in the leading university of the country, and the thirty-three-year-old professor resolved to do everything possible to prove himself worthy.

Enthusiastically Mendeleev began to prepare his lectures. He buried himself in books and journals. He got out all the notes he had made on his work during years of study and investigation. He submerged himself in an endless sea of facts, experiments and laws, established during the course of decades by hundreds of chemists. There was enough material for a dozen university courses. But, strangely enough, the deeper Mendeleev plunged into his long familiar science, the harder his task seemed to him.

In the autumn he began his course. His lectures had an enormous success. The lecture hall was packed like the auditorium of a theatre when some famous actor is to appear. People came from other departments to hear him - from the law school, the medical school, the department of history. They came from other institutions. They flocked to the lecture room and sat waiting long before the time scheduled for the lecture to begin. They stood in the aisles and crowded round the door in the hall outside. They pushed in around the experimental table at the front of the hall.

Such a triumph had rarely fallen to the lot of a university professor.

Yet, deep in his heart, Mendeleev was not satisfied.

He began to work on a new book dealing with fundamentals of chemistry. He called it Principles of Chemistry. He wrote fast and easily, using the notes he had made for his lectures. His students looked forward eagerly to having these brilliant lectures in print. But Mendeleev still was not satisfied. The book was not what he wanted it to be.

He had begun to have the feeling that the science of chemistry was like a thick forest without any trails or roads. He felt as if he were wandering from tree to tree in this forest, describing each one of them separately. And there were so many thousands of them!

By this time chemists knew 63 different elements. Combinations of these elements gave hundreds and thousands of different substances: oxides, salts, acids, bases ....

There were gases, liquids, crystals, metals .... There were colourless substances and substances of a blinding brilliance, with and without odours, hard and soft, bitter and sweet, heavy and light, stable and unstable - not one exactly like another.

Chemists had thoroughly investigated all the enormous variety of things of which the world is made. They knew hundreds of details about each separate thing. They even knew exactly how to make these compounds and which was the cheapest method.

They knew the colour of every ore, the form of its crystals, its specific gravity, boiling and melting points - all these and much more had been measured, weighed, described in text books and reference books.

They had studied the effects of heat and cold on all these compounds; how an electric current or pressure affected them; how they behaved in a vacuum. They had tested how they react with oxygen and hydrogen, with acids and with alkalis. How much heat or cold is expended in the process.

One could spend weeks, months even, describing the infinite number of chemical substances and not cover them all. And the more talk there was about it, the less the listener understood chemistry. There was no uniformity in this chaos, no general system. Could it be that all this material our world is made of was arranged in so haphazard and accidental a way?

Mendeleev wanted to unfold before his students a single, orderly picture of things; wanted to show them the chief laws governing the construction of the universe. But he found neither unity nor order in his beloved science.

True, all this enormous variety of materials could be produced from a few elements. But the confusion and disorder began here, in this little group of fundamental substances.

There was no explanation of the fact that the metal magnesium was more inflammable than coal; that platinum could lie for thousands of years and never change, while fluorine gas so loved chemical change that it would even eat through the glass of the vessel in which it was stored. There seemed to be no regularity in it all. And if the elements had had exactly the opposite properties of those they have - for example, if platinum corroded glass and fluorine was the most stable of all substances - chemists would have felt no astonishment.

Every element with all its individual properties seemed a purely chance arrangement of matter. There seemed to be no connection whatever among these primitive forms of matter, or at least that appeared to be the case with the majority of them.

Dmitri Mendeleev
(1834 - 1907)

This did not bother most chemists at all.

"If there is no natural order in the world of matter," they reasoned, "then we shall list the elements in any order we like."

They usually began with oxygen, as there is more of this element in the world than of any other. But some chemists preferred to begin with hydrogen as the lightest of the elements. And you could just as well begin with iron, because it is the most useful, or with gold because it is one of the costliest, or with the very rare indium because it is the most recently discovered element.

What difference does it make where you enter into a thick, tangled forest? After you have taken only a few steps all traces of any path or road will be lost.

Mendeleev did not want to enter this maze haphazardly. As he prepared his university course on Principles of Chemistry he kept continually searching for a general law, a natural order governing all the elements. He was convinced there must be some such law, some hidden uniformity among the elements, so different in appearance one from another.

And that was what he was looking for.

2. Atomic weight

It did not, after all, require any special acuteness to notice a striking similarity among some of the elements. Besides the twin elements, related elements, in the group of 'inflammable' metals discovered by Davy and Bunsen, there were many others which had been unknown to chemists for a long time, for example, fluorine, bromine, iodine; and the alkaline earth metals, magnesium, calcium, strontium and barium.

"This cannot be due to chance," Mendeleev reasoned. "There must be some hidden inter-dependence, some kind of connection between all the elements. There must be a fundamental characteristic common to all elements without exception, some characteristic which indicates both their similarities and their differences. If we knew this we could arrange all the elements and at the same time also arrange all their infinite combinations in regular order, just as soldiers are lined up according to size."

What could this fundamental characteristic be, this decisive indicator? The colour of the elemnt perhaps? But how decide what colour an element is? Take phosphorus, for example. There is a red phosphorus and a yellow phosphorus. Or take iodine - in its solid state it has a dark brown, metallic sheen; but if it is heated the very same iodine appears as a violet vapour. And yellow gold when

"If we knew this we could arrange all the elements and at the same time also arrange all their infinite combinations in regular order, just as soldiers are lined up according to size."

rolled out into a very thin leaf becomes bluish green and transparent, like mica.

No, colour is evidently too unstable and secondary a quality to depend on if we are going to establish natural order among the elements.

How about their specific gravity then? But this is an even less dependable quality. For the moment a thing is even slightly heated its specific gravity changes.

(Specific gravity is a measure of the amount by which one element is heavier than another. Usually the weights of various substances are compared with the weight of a like amount of water. Thus, for example, the specific gravity of iron at a temperature of 15°C. (60°F.) is 7.8; this means that 1 cubic centimetre of iron is 7.8 times heavier than 1 cubic centimetre of water.)

For the same reason neither conductivity of heat nor of electricity, nor the magnetic or any other of a number of properties will do.

Obviously there must be some other fundamental indicator which never changes, without which no element can possibly be imagined to exist - an indicator as characteristic of an element as is the face of each individual human being; an indicator which an element never loses even when it combines with other elements to form new, complex substances with new properties.

Was there, could there be, such an indicator?

This question haunted Mendeleev; it never left him. He thought, he figured, he compared. And there really was such an indicator, such a characteristic all the time. It was well known to Mendeleev and to all other chemists; but not one had attached any importance to it. It was called Atomic Weight.

Every chemical element has its own, strictly defined atomic weight, determined by experiments. Whether hot or cold, yellow or red, dark or light in shade, this remains always the same. Atomic weight never changes under any circumstances. It is the element's label.

The atomic weight of an element indicates how many times heavier is its atom, that is, each one of the smallest particles composing the element, than an atom of hydrogen, the very lightest of the elements. Oxygen, for example, has an atomic weight of 16. That means its atoms are 16 times heavier than an atom of hydrogen. The atomic weight of gold is 197; that is, its atoms are 197 times heavier than the atoms of hydrogen.

The size of the atoms, those tiniest particles of which an element is composed, determines their atomic weight. All the atoms of a given element are absolutely identical. Every atom of any given element differs from every atom of any other given element by its size, by its weight. Wouldn't it seem, then, that all the other differences which characterise the different elements should be dependent precisely on this fundamental indicator?

Mendeleev came to this conclusion after careful comparison of the properties of all the elements. And he surmised that in this lay the key to the laws determining their similarities and their differences. It was the key he had been looking for, the key to uniformity and order in the world of matter. All that was necessary was to know how to use this key.

The indications as to how this might be done were vague and confused. To guard against mistakes and to help see more clearly the connection between the different elements, Mendeleev cut 63 squares of cardboard and wrote on each one of them the name of one of the elements, its chief characteristics and its atomic weight. He arranged the cards in different combinations, changed their places, looked for similarities and differences, seeking to find some general order, some one single law governing all these substances.

Day and night, on the rostrum, in the laboratory, at his desk at home or walking along the street, the thought of this Natural System of the elements never left his mind. One evening, one of his students tells us, he had sat for a long, long time playing at his chemical solitaire, until finally he fell asleep without having accomplished anything. But his brain, excited by this long mental strain, evidently did not stop working when he went to sleep. For he dreamed that he saw his system all written out in the form of a table, orderly, irrefutable, clear. Next morning he got up and wrote it down.

3. The elements lined up

It would of course be hard to check that story now. But, whether or not it is true, at any rate the Natural or Periodic System of the Elements was discovered in the spring of the year 1869. As time went on Mendeleev worked it out in detail and announced it to the Russian Physico-Chemical Society.

Of what did his discovery consist?

All the chemical elements fall into a natural order. It begins with hydrogen, the lightest element, composed of the smallest atoms. Its atomic weight is 1. Last on the list comes the metal uranium, consisting of the heaviest atoms. Its atomic weight is 238. Between them are arranged all the remaining elements with atoms gradually increasing in weight. And all the characteristics of any given element, its outward appearance, its stability, its capacity to form combinations with other elements, and also the characteristics of such compounds, depend precisely on where the element stands on the list.

Now it is a curious fact that the elements, when arranged according to their atomic weights, fall automatically into similar groups, having similar characteristics; they form families of related substances.

Picture to yourself, by way of illustration, a crowd of people of all sizes and dressed in costumes of every known colour. At first glance there appears to be nothing but motley disorder. But suppose the people are ordered to arrange themselves in rows, strictly according to size, and that, when this is done, all the random variety disappears of itself. The first seven people, the smallest, turn out to be dressed respectively in red, orange, yellow, green, blue, indigo, violet. The next group of seven wear the same colours arranged in the same order. And so on to the end, to the last, tallest family.

It is discovered that the colours are repeated for every seven people. And if every family is placed behind one another the original motley-coloured crowd of people fall into identical series of red, orange, yellow, etc. And there seems to be the strictest order in the matter of size, too, from the very smallest of the family group in the front row to the tallest in the back row at the opposite end.

That is approximately the order Mendeleev discovered among the elements when he arranged them according to their atomic weights.

Every seven elements find their characteristics periodically repeated. Similar elements all stand 'behind one another', in a regular series or groups.

I	II	III	IV	V	VI	VII	VIII
1.Hydrogen 1.00							
2.Lithium 6.94	3.Berylllium 9.02	4.Boron 10.82	5.Carbon 12.00	6.Nitrogen 14.00	7.Oxygen 16.00	8.Fluorine 19.00	
9.Sodium 23.00	10.Magnesium 40.07	11.Aluminium 26.97	12.Silicon 28.06	13.Phosphorus 31.04	14.Sulphur 32.07	15.Chlorine 35.45	
16.Potassium 39.10	17.Calcium 40.07	18.Eka-boron 44	19.Titanium 47.90	20.Vanadium 51.00	21.Chromium 52.01	22.Manganese 54.93	23.Iron 55.84 24.Cobalt 58.97 25.Nickel 58.08 26.Copper 63.57
26.Copper 63.57	27.Zinc 63.38	28.Eka-aluminium 68	20.Eka-silicon 72	30.Arsenic 74.96	31.Selenium 79.2	32.Bromine 79.92	
33. Rubidium 85.45	34.Strontium 87.63	35.Yttrium 88.9	36.Zirconium 91.25	37.Columbium 93.5	38.Molybdenium 96.0	39. ?	40.Ruthenium 101.7 41.Rhodium 102.9 42. Palladium 106.7 43.Silver 102.88
43.Silver 102.88	44.Cadmium 112.4	45.Indium 114.8	46.Tin 118.7	47.Antimony 121.76	48.Tellurium 127.5	49.Iodine 126.92	
50.Caesium	51.Barium	52.	53.	54.	55.	56.	

Mendeleev's Periodic System of Elements as it looked in 1870.

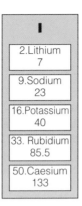

I
2.Lithium 7
9.Sodium 23
16.Potassium 40
33. Rubidium 85.5
50.Caesium 133

So the light metal, lithium, with an atomic weight of 7, comes second, just after hydrogen. And the ninth is sodium, with an atomic weight of 23; also a metal, also very light - like lithium - and active, inflammable, readily uniting with other elements.

In the sixteenth place again comes a light, inflammable metal, potassium, with an atomic weight of 40. And so on at regular intervals, or periods, the other alkali metals range themselves in the same order; rubidium, with an atomic weight of 85.5, caesium with an atomic weight of 133.

In this order the properties of the lightest metals gradually change from the top down. The lightest, lithium, is also the most stable. If it is put into water it flares up and makes a hissing noise, but does not burn up like potassium and caesium. Lithium also rusts less rapidly than the other two related elements when exposed to air. Sodium is more active than lithium; and caesium, the last in the series and the heaviest in weight, makes the most violent chemical combinations of all. Caesium cannot remain exposed to the air for a single second. It is immediately consumed by spontaneous combustion.

All the elements are arranged in such more or less related groups or families. And in every group the characteristics of the elements and the characteristics of their countless compounds change gradually and in strict order along with the increase in their atomic weights.

So the world of matter, chaotic at first glance, actually displays a marvellous orderliness. Mendeleev saw behind the outward diversity an inner uniformity, an iron law of regularity. He called this the Periodic Law.

4. Chemistry or magic?

It may seem strange that up to Mendeleev's time no one had noticed this natural connection between elements. It would seem to be the most natural thing in the world to do: merely to make a list of the elements, arranging them according to their atomic weights. Then the Periodic Law would have revealed itself. How did it happen that no chemist except Mendeleev had the idea of doing such a simple thing? Apparently it would have been very easy to do this, as easy as to arrange them, say, alphabetically.

Well, other chemists had tried to do it, but Mendeleev was the only one who discovered the Periodic Law and used it for the further development of science. For, as a matter of fact, it was not such a simple thing to do after all.

The real connection between the elements turned out to be incredibly complicated, like something written in an obscure code. It took exceptional penetration and imagination to figure out the secret of the chemical code.

Picture an investigator who has come into possession of a valuable coded document, together with the key to the code. He eagerly opens up both documents expecting to read the secret writing. But when he begins to compare them he suddenly discovers that a trick has been played on him: his key is useless. Some symbols are mixed up and some are totally lacking. There are only 15 or 20 symbols instead of 26, one for every letter in the alphabet, which he should have.

Let us suppose, for example, that the first symbol stands for 'a' - there is no way of telling whether the second one stands for 'b', 'c', or 'd'. And these gaps, this absence of symbols, makes the whole key worthless, because it is impossible to be sure to what letter of the alphabet any of the rest of the symbols correspond.

When Mendeleev discovered the Periodic Law he was in the same sort of difficult situation. He arranged the elements according to their atomic weights; but he did not know that the atomic weights assigned to some of them were inexact. With the methods used in those days some of the weights were bound to be wrong, and the mistakes were not discovered until many years later. Such elements with false labels were accordingly assigned to the wrong places in Mendeleev's arrangement, and this of course spoiled the natural order of the elements. Groups of similar elements were broken up by the presence of stray sheep in their midst.

The blanks were still more confusing. Mendeleev knew of the existence of only 63 elements, and he could not know whether or not other elements as yet undiscovered existed in nature. Remember our row of people in coloured costumes, arranged according to size. Suppose five or ten people stepped out of the ranks. The colours would than be mixed up and there would no longer be any regular order of succession. That was the way it was in the case of the elements.

It was hard to get the elements which were known to Mendeleev to fit into his table. They huddled up and broke ranks like untrained recruits. Mendeleev, by sheer force of his genius, forced them into their true places and resolutely brought order out of chaos.

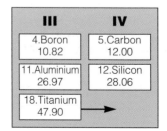

III	IV
4.Boron 10.82	5.Carbon 12.00
11.Aluminium 26.97	12.Silicon 28.06
18.Titanium 47.90 →	

Under the element boron, which came fourth, and aluminium, which came eleventh, was the element titanium in the eighteenth place, according to the arrangement. The space between them seemed to be correct - exactly six elements, a complete period. But titanium's characteristics made it a complete stranger in the group of boron and aluminium. It belonged rather in a neighbouring group, the carbon group. So Mendeleev decided to move it out of the eighteenth place.

III	IV
4.Boron 10.82	5.Carbon 12.00
11.Aluminium 26.97	12.Silicon 28.06
18.Eka-boron 44	19.Titanium 47.90
28.Eka-aluminium 68	20.Eka-silicon 72
35.Yttrium 88.9	36.Zirconium 91.25

"That's not chemistry, that's magic! It's like trying to predict the future from dreams!"

"There should be another element here, one we have not yet discovered", he said. "An element similar to boron and aluminium."

So he left an open space. When titanium was moved up it was then in its own related group and pushing it up pushed all the following elements along too.

By using these empty squares Mendeleev got the elements so grouped in his table that they did not spoil the Periodic Law.

He did not leave the squares entirely empty. He filed them with new elements he had himself invented. He even gave them names: eka-boron, meaning boron plus one. Eka is Sanscrit for one. Eka-aluminium, eka-silicon. And he foretold the characteristics of these elements which he had never seen, elements which were born out of his own imagination. He even described how they would look, their atomic weights and the compounds they would form with other elements.

There was no magic, nothing supernatural about these prophecies. For, you see, these unknown elements in the empty squares were not solitary individuals. They stood in definite places among similar elements in the table and it was possible, therefore, simply to calculate their characteristics although no one in the world had ever seen them.

Mendeleev did this because he was firmly convinced of the validity of the Periodic Law he had discovered. But many other chemists thought him impudent and presumptuous.

"The idea of inventing elements that do not exist, then endowing these ghosts with imagined properties and including all this stuff in a course in an exact science which deals only with existing substances, with tangible, indisputable facts! That's not chemistry, that's magic! It's like trying to predict the future from dreams!"

That is practically the way most scientists of his day felt about Mendeleev's system and its prediction of elements.

Only facts could convince these sceptics.

Years went by and the empty squares in Mendeleev's table were still occupied only by ghosts, by imaginary substances. Nobody took them seriously. Worse than that, they were almost completely forgotten.

5. The prophecies are fulfiled

On September 20, 1875, Academician Wurtz appeared before the regular session of the French Academy of Science in Paris and asked, in the name of one of his students, Lecoq de Boisbaudran, that a letter which had been sent to the secretary of the Academy three weeks previously be read aloud. This was done. The letter ran as follows:

"Night before last, the 27th of August, 1875," Lecoq de Boisbaudran had written, "between three and four in the morning I discovered a new element in a mineral zinc sulphide from the Pierrefitte mine in the Pyrenees..."

A new element! At last. It had been a long time since chemists had heard such an announcement.

Lecoq de Boisbaudran had specialised for many years in spectral analysis of chemical substances. And here at last was a brilliant reward for his devotion to his work. He had 'captured' an unfamiliar violet ray, the indication of an unknown element.

That night, on the 27th of August, he had only a few drops of the solution of zinc salt in which the microscopic bit of the new element was contained. Lecoq decided therefore not to announce his discovery immediately. But to make sure he would get credit for having first discovered the new element, in case someone else also discovered it in the meantime, he hurried off to the Academy and addressed to Wurtz a sealed package containing the first announcement of his discovery.

$\dfrac{1}{1,000}$ **gm of Gallium**

Now three weeks later, he had accumulated a whole milligram of the new element, that is, a thousandth part of a gram. He could safely assert without fear of being mistaken that it was really a new element.

He wanted to call the new element gallium in honour of his native land. Gallia is the old Latin name of France.

Lecoq de Boisbaudran wrote that he was continuing his investigations and would have more to report in due course. All the information he could give at the moment was that, chemically, gallium seemed very much like the familiar aluminium.

When the report of this session of the French Academy of Science reached far away St. Petersburg, Mendeleev was thunderstruck. This element which a Frenchman had found in a mine in the Pyrenees was not a new element at all. Mendeleev had discovered it five years earlier. It was simply eka-aluminium! Everything fitted into place, even Mendeleev's prophecy that eka-aluminium, since it was very volatile, would be discovered by spectral analysis.

In the old days people would have called this a miracle. Mendeleev was himself deeply stirred by this brilliant fulfilment of his prophecies. He immediately dispatched a letter to the Academy of Science in Paris, saying:

"Gallium is the eka-aluminium I predicted. Its atomic weight is about 68, its specific gravity about 5.9. Investigate and see if this is not correct."

Chemists all over the world now eagerly followed the reports of the French Academy of Science. It was an extraordinarily interesting situation: one scientist, sitting in his study in St. Petersburg, makes a prophecy and another in Paris, working with flasks and test-tubes, performs an experiment and carries out exact measurements to confirm his far-away colleague's prediction!

However, there was a dispute about the specific gravity of gallium. When Lecoq de Boisbaudran got a sufficiently large quantity of the new element in pure form - one fifteenth of a gram - he determined its specific gravity and found it to be 4.7.

"That's not correct!" insisted Mendeleev far away in St. Petersburg. "It should be 5.9. Your specimen is evidently not sufficiently pure."

Boisbaudran tried again, this time with a bigger piece.

"Yes," he finally acknowledged. "Monsieur Mendeleev is right. The specific gravity of gallium is 5.9."

This was the first great victory of the Periodic Law. It was followed almost immediately by others. Two Scandinavian experimenters, Nilson and Cleve, discovered a new element in the rare mineral, gadolinite. They named it scandium.

As soon as they began to investigate its characteristics it was evident that this, too, was an old acquaintance, eka-boron, from the 'empty' eighteenth square of Mendeleev's table.

But the most brilliant triumph came to Mendeleev in 1885 when a German chemist, Winkler, discovered another new element in a silver ore from the Himmelsfuerst mine. Winkler named the new element germanium. This germanium fitted exactly into the empty twenty-ninth square of Mendeleev's table, temporarily occupied by eka-silicon. The characteristics of both these elements, the one foretold by Mendeleev and the actual one discovered by Winkler, coincided so exactly that it was positively uncanny.

Judge for yourself. In 1870 Mendeleev predicted that a new element would be discovered belonging to the carbon and chromium group, and it would be a dark grey metal. Fifteen years later Winkler finds in a mine near Freiburg an element similar in many respects to carbon and chromium and it proves to be a dark grey substance with a metallic lustre.

"Its atomic weight will be about 72," predicted Mendeleev.

"Its atomic weight is 72.73," confirmed Winkler.

"Its specific gravity will be about 5.5," predicted Mendeleev.

72	72.73
5.5	5.47
4.7	4.7
1.9	1.887
...	...
...	...

"5.47," confirmed Winkler.

Mendeleev: "The oxide of the new element, that is, the compound it makes with oxygen, will be hard to melt, it will be very hard to melt it even in a very hot fire. The specific gravity of this oxide will be 4.7."

Winkler: "Exactly so."

Mendeleev: "The specific gravity of a compound of the new element with chlorine will be about 1.9."

Winkler: "1.887."

And so on and so on.

6. No more blank spaces

From this time on, the Natural System of the Elements was universally accepted. It was now clear to everyone that simple substances are not unrelated, accidental phenomena - that between them there is a close connection, a unity of all forms of matter.

Formerly chemists had no way of knowing whether all the elements had been discovered or whether they might expect that new elements with entirely unexpected characteristics would keep on being discovered indefinitely.

Now, thanks to Mendeleev, the picture of the material construction of the universe was incomparably clearer and more distinct. A chemist felt quite as confident of his bearings in the world of the elements as does the present-day geographer among the seas and continents of our globe, which has been explored from end to end.

Supplied with accurate maps, no geographer of our day would set out to look for unknown islands in the Atlantic ocean between Newfoundland and Ireland, or for mountain peaks on the plains of South America. He knows they are not there and cannot be there.

Just so, chemists armed with Mendeleev's table will not look for any new alkali metals between potassium and sodium, nor for any new elements between scandium and titanium, because no such elements are possible. It would be contrary to the Periodic Law.

From Mendeleev's table, chemists were able to judge more or less accurately how many elements there are in the world. They now knew approximately how many elements were still escaping them, hiding in rare minerals in some secluded corner of the world. The blank spaces in the world of matter were disappearing one after another, because now it was known where the absentees were and how to look for them.

Yet there were still quite a few surprises in store.

Remember the puzzling sun element, helium, which we were talking about in Chapter Three? What became of it? Was a place found for it in Mendeleev's table? Had Mendeleev also described its characteristics without having seen it, as he did gallium, scandium and germanium?

No, Mendeleev did not have much faith in the sun element. His theory was that one of the known elements, iron or oxygen perhaps, gave the unfamiliar yellow line. He considered it probable that due to the high temperature of the sun and the enormous pressures prevailing, these elements might give out rays of a different colour from those they emit under conditions prevailing on our earth.

The day came, a never-to-be-forgotten day for science, when the riddle of helium was solved once and for all. Mendeleev was still alive. He thought he had suffered a big defeat on that question, but it was the greatest of all his scientific victories.

7. A prophet without honour in his own country

The triumphs of the Periodic Law brought Mendeleev world-wide fame. Many foreign universities conferred honorary degrees on him. He was elected a member of academies of science and scientific societies. English scientists invited him to London to deliver the Faraday lecture - traditionally given only by the greatest scientists. They also presented him with the Davy gold medal.

All the civilised countries of the world honoured the author of the Periodic Law and vied with one another in acclaiming him for his scientific work.

Only in his own country, at that time under the rule of an absolute monarch, did Mendeleev fail to receive the recognition he deserved. Even worse than that - protégés of the tsar dared to insult and humiliate the great chemist.

When his name was presented for election to the Russian Academy of Science he was rejected. All kinds of insignificant toadies and office-seekers were members of the Academy, and the greatest Russian scientist that had ever lived was rejected!

They also presented Mendeleev with the Davy gold medal.

Later a tsarist minister named Delyanov drove him out of the university for having 'dared' to present a student petition for improving the conditions at the university. And for many years this world-famous old scientist had no laboratory in which to work.

However, Mendeleev never shut himself up in his laboratory. He was an ardent patriot and devoted all his energy and talents to the benefit of his country. Yet nearly all his practical proposals were rejected.

At that time the oil industry was just beginning to develop in the Caucasus. Mendeleev insisted that petroleum should be used with the greatest care, since it is a priceless chemical. He said that its use for heating boilers was as irrational as it would be to stoke fires with pound notes. He wanted the production and treatment of crude petroleum to be carried out only in the strictest scientific way. But few there were who would listen to Mendeleev. The owners of the oil fields obtained and used up the crude petroleum in the most barbaric way, refusing to give any thought to the problems of the future.

Mendeleev went about proving to people that Russia needed a tremendous chemical industry. But right up to the October revolution (1917) Russia possessed only a few small, poorly-equipped plants.

Mendeleev dreamed of exploring the stratosphere and once made a balloon ascent without the aid of a pilot.

Mendeleev dreamed of exploring the stratosphere and once made a balloon ascent without the aid of a pilot. He demanded that the Arctic and the Northern Sea routes be developed and worked out projects for ice-cutters. After spending some time in the Ural anthracite mines Mendeleev proposed underground gasification of coal. He showed how the coal could be ignited right in the mine, thus turning the coal into inflammable gas at the source and sparing the miners the difficult job of digging it and carrying it above ground.

But his brilliant proposals and projects found no support. Most tsarist hangers-on were interested only in soft jobs and money. Few could be found who took any interest in the development of science and the promotion of the general welfare of the country.

It was only after Mendeleev's death, when a new life began in Russia, that the Five Year Plan for economic and technological development of the USSR began to put into practice many of the great scientist's ideas.

CHAPTER 5
Noble Gases

1. A thousandth of a gram

In this chapter we are at last going to tell you about the sun element helium. It was astronomers who first discovered helium, you will recall. Next, physicists had a hand in its fate, then chemists and finally geologists. It was a marvellous chain of discoveries and brilliant conjectures. This is the way it happened.

In the 1880's an English physicist, Rayleigh, was performing a long series of experiments with gases. For certain reasons, which it would take too long to explain here, Rayleigh had to determine with great accuracy how much a litre of each gas weighed. This is what is called its density.

Rayleigh first weighed hydrogen, the lightest of all. Next oxygen. Then he began on nitrogen. He wanted to make his measurements the most accurate of any ever made by physicists. He was not going to let one bubble of gas, no matter how small it was, escape him as he weighed. He took a thousand precautions to make sure the gas to be weighed was absolutely pure.

It is not hard to get pure nitrogen from the air. Ever since the time of Scheele and Lavoisier everyone knew that air was four parts nitrogen to one part oxygen. All that was necessary was to get rid of the oxygen, and a little carbonic acid gas and water vapour which are always present in air, and you had pure nitrogen.

Rayleigh proceeded in this way. He passed the air through a series of chemical traps: in one the carbonic acid gas was absorbed, another took out all the oxygen, a third absorbed the water vapour.

Rayleigh also used sulphuric acid but he used other substances besides, and these drew out all the oxygen, carbonic acid gas, and moisture.

This left him with pure nitrogen and Rayleigh weighed it.

No good experimenter ever hesitates to repeat his own experiments any number of times to avoid the possibility of mistakes. Rayleigh was an exceptionally conscientious and accurate experimenter, but it was still possible that one of the traps was not working as it should. Some of the impurities might have got through, or the rubber tube might have sprung one of those traitorous little holes, minute, invisible to the eye, but big enough just the same to let in some impure air from the outside.

So, as a check on his results, Rayleigh decided to try obtaining nitrogen by another method instead of from the air. If the density of both agreed, then it would mean everything was in order and his results were correct. He could be confident that the work had been done carefully, that the nitrogen was free from impurities, and that there was nothing wrong with his apparatus.

A chemist friend of his, Ramsay, advised him to obtain nitrogen from ammonia gas. This was a good method and Rayleigh immediately tried it. He extracted the nitrogen from ammonia, purified it according to all the rules, then weighed it.

Imagine his chagrin when the weights of the two gases, both nitrogen, did not agree.

A litre of nitrogen obtained from the air weighed 1.2572 grams. A litre of nitrogen obtained from ammonia weighed 1.2560 - that is, 1/1000 of a gram less.

There must have been a mistake in his work, Rayleigh thought. It was not a very big difference, 1/1000 of a gram, but still it was a difference. There must have been an error somewhere.

He went carefully all over his apparatus - tested vessel after vessel, trap after trap, the tubes, the pump, the scales.

Then he set about obtaining his samples of nitrogen again, one from air, the other from ammonia. He purified both samples with the greatest accuracy - and again the two weights did not agree by 1/1000 of a gram.

The difference was so slight - you might think it could be waved aside and ignored. But Rayleigh could not bring himself to ignore even the smallest error.

He was annoyed and irritated by this disagreement. He kept on with his experiments with nitrogen but could not get a step further. There were dozens of other new and interesting problems in physics inviting his attention, but he could not take any time for them; he was so busy with his nitrogen difficulty that he had become a chemist, much against his will.

One day while Rayleigh was looking with unconcealed disgust at the pages on which he had set down the results of the last weighing, he happened to notice the current number of the English scientific periodical 'Nature' lying nearby.

"I'll write them a letter!" he resolved.

And without a moment's delay he scribbled off a letter to the editors then and there. He told them about the bad results he had got with his nitrogen and challenged chemists to point out to him where he made any mistake that would explain this stubborn disagreement.

Then he sent off his letter and waited to see what would happen. Maybe the chemists would get him out of this impasse.

Lord Rayleigh
(1842 - 1919)

2. Heavy nitrogen and light nitrogen

Sir William Ramsay
(1852 - 1916)

Answers to his letter soon began to arrive. Among them was one from Ramsay. The chemists gave the disappointed physicist lots of good advice but unfortunately none of it helped him at all. The difference between the weights of the two gases stayed right where it was. Worse than that, when Rayleigh changed the conditions of the experiment the difference was even greater than before.

Rayleigh spent two years on his stubborn gas. He tried everything. He passed an electric discharge through both the air nitrogen and the ammonia nitrogen. He shut the nitrogen up in a tightly sealed container for eight whole months. But neither electricity nor time changed the properties of the two gases. The difference in density remained the same.

Rayleigh tried obtaining nitrogen from other sources. He got it from laughing gas, from oxide of nitrogen, from urea. In every case the weight of the gas obtained in these ways agreed with that of the nitrogen obtained from ammonia; but the nitrogen from the air continued to weigh more.

Next Rayleigh tried getting nitrogen from the air by a different process. He had previously passed the air over incandescent copper. As the metal burned it took all the oxygen out of the air, leaving pure nitrogen. Now he tried using incandescent iron or some other substance that readily absorbs oxygen. But the density of the air nitrogen did not vary in the slightest degree. It was still just a little heavier than that obtained from ammonia.

After all the many experiments he had performed Rayleigh could still see no sign of light ahead. He felt as if he had run into a thick wall which he could neither get through nor go around.

But at least he felt sure now that the difference was not due to any mistake on his part. It was nature's fault, not his. It was indisputably evident that the nitrogen obtained from air was actually heavier than the nitrogen obtained from chemical compounds.

But why? How could one and the same thing have two different weights? That was the tormenting riddle that gave him no peace of mind.

3. "Look in the old journals"

In 1894 Rayleigh gave a lecture at the Royal Society in London on his experiments with nitrogen. After the meeting, Ramsay, the chemist, went up to him and offered to help him.

"Two years ago when you wrote that letter to 'Nature', I couldn't understand why you got that discrepancy. But I think it is quite clear now. There is some heavy impurity in the nitrogen from the air - some unknown gas. If you will permit me I'd like to try to continue your work."

Rayleigh was only too glad to have his help, though he thought the supposition about an unknown gas improbable. Thousands of investigators had analysed air over and over again and they had always found only nitrogen, oxygen and a small quantity of carbonic acid gas and water vapour. Where could the strange gas come from?

He discussed the matter with a number of his colleagues in the Society, among them, Dewar, a physicist.

"Look through some of the old journals," said Dewar. "It seems to me Henry Cavendish stated somewhere that the nitrogen of the air was not homogeneous."

"Cavendish!" exclaimed Rayleigh in astonishment. "A hundred years ago!"

"Yes," Dewar insisted. "It seems to me that in one of his earlier works about the composition of air there is some remark to that effect. Look for it."

"I certainly shall, this very day!" said Rayleigh.

To think he might have been anticipated by a hundred years!

Henry Cavendish
(1737 - 1810)

4. Henry Cavendish's experiment

A lonely, eccentric, excessively shy man, Henry Cavendish lived in London during the second half of the 18th Century. He was so afraid of people that when they talked to him he would blush, utter shrill sounds and stumble away as fast as he could. Or if he did muster up courage to answer, he would stammer and get his words all tangled up like a little child just learning to talk.

Cavendish lived like a hermit in his big, uncomfortable house, only rarely appearing in company. This reserved and silent man had only one interest - science, the investigation of nature. For fifty years, day after day, without rest or recreation or holidays, Cavendish worked, calculated, experimented.

He discovered the composition of water.

He was the first to calculate the weight of the earth.

At the same time as Scheele and Lavoisier, he was studying the composition of the air and the properties of oxygen and nitrogen.

Cavendish was careful and sceptical, and in no hurry to publish the results of his experiments. Much remained buried in his archives. Some of his work was simply forgotten. So it happened that several generations later John Rayleigh, racking his brain over the riddle of 'heavy' air, never suspected that he could find the answer to the puzzle by looking through the yellowed pages of the Reports of the Royal Society for the year 1785.

There Cavendish described the following experiment:

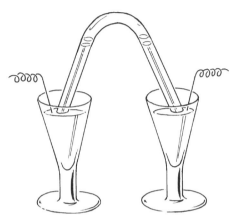

Henry Cavendish's experiment.

He sent electric sparks, tiny artificial flashes of lightning, through a glass tube filled with air. The electricity caused the two component parts of the air, nitrogen and oxygen, to unite and form a chemical compound, a new gas, with a suffocating odour. He kept drawing this gas out of the tube, absorbing it with a special solution.

Now, since there is only one-fifth as much oxygen as nitrogen in the air, the oxygen was exhausted long before the nitrogen. So he added pure oxygen and again passed the electric sparks through. He repeated this until finally nearly all the nitrogen had united with oxygen in the form of the new, suffocating gas, and had been absorbed by the alkali solution.

One little bubble of nitrogen, however, stubbornly remained in the tube and was not absorbed by the alkali. Cavendish tried adding more pure oxygen over and over again, but in vain. Passing electric charges through had no effect. No more suffocating gas was produced. The little bubble of nitrogen, no bigger than a pea, just swam round on top of the solution and refused to unite with the oxygen.

"From this experiment I have come to the conclusion," wrote Cavendish, "that the nitrogen in the air is not homogeneous. Part of it [1/120] acts in a different way from the larger, principal part. It is probable that nitrogen is not one uniform substance but is a mixture of two different substances." (Cavendish was an exponent of the phlogiston theory and he called nitrogen 'phlogisticated air'.)

When Rayleigh had read as far as that in the old journal, he put his hands to his head and rushed pell-mell to his laboratory to repeat Cavendish's old experiment.

5. What is air made of?

Meanwhile William Ramsay, the chemist, colleague of Rayleigh in the Royal Society, was not wasting his time either.

He reasoned very simply: There is in the air some impurity which we do not know about. There is only one way to discover it: take a definite amount of air and extract all its component parts one after the other. If there is something left over after this has been done, that means there is some unknown gas in the air.

Ramsay passed the air through a number of chemical traps and easily separated out the oxygen, water vapour and carbonic acid gas. The nitrogen was left. He had found a trap for it, too. Several years earlier he had discovered quite accidentally, that nitrogen has a great affinity for incandescent magnesium chips, the metal used for photography in dimly lighted places. So now, using this knowledge, he blew the nitrogen over incandescent magnesium.

Most of the nitrogen was absorbed during the first passage through the tube that had magnesium in it, but a little got by. So again he passed the remainder over the incandescent chips. There was still less of the gas left. He repeated the operation - and weighed the remainder.

It was definitely heavier than ordinary nitrogen found in the air. Ordinarily nitrogen was 14 times as heavy as hydrogen. This gas was 14.88 times as heavy as hydrogen.

Ramsay, feeling that he was on the right track, passed it through the tube of magnesium again. This time, too, part of the gas was trapped but the remainder had grown still heavier. Every time he performed the experiment, the quantity of gas left became smaller, but its density increased. It reached 16, then 18, 19.... At 20 it stood still. And precisely at this point the quantity of the gas remained stationary, too. Evidently all the nitrogen had been absorbed and whatever was left consisted of the heavy, unknown impurity on which the magnesium did not act.

All summer Ramsay kept on passing air through an absorber until he got a tenth of a litre of the new gas.

Rayleigh, who was using the old Cavendish method, did not get on so rapidly. At the end of the summer of 1894 he had collected only half a cubic centimetre of the heavy impurity. The important thing was that both investigators, working independently and using different methods, had obtained identical results.

Now all they had to do was to find out the 'opinion' of the spectroscope about the new gas. They fused electrodes into a glass tube, filled it with the new gas, and switched on the current. The gas glowed with a beautiful, cold light. Its spectrum showed red, green, and blue lines - all new lines, never before seen by any spectroscopist.

On August 13, 1894, Rayleigh and Ramsay went to Oxford where there was a meeting of British scientific research workers and asked permission to make an announcement which was not scheduled on the programme.

The Cavendish Laboratory in Cambridge.

"We have discovered a new element," they stated. "It is all around us, everywhere. Along with oxygen and nitrogen it is one of the component parts of the air we breathe."

6. A hermit element

If a bomb had burst above the heads of these scientists gathered at Oxford they would have been less astonished than they were by this announcement.

An unknown element in the air! Huge quantities of it in every laboratory, in every university hall, all over the world - and no one had ever suspected it!

For a whole century investigators had been collecting rare minerals from all over the world in an effort to capture the last elements still hidden from chemists. And they had overlooked an unknown substance that was right under their noses!

How could this have happened? For there was a considerable quantity of the gas in the air - one litre in every hundred.

When Cavendish first picked up the trail, people had just begun to realise that there were two kinds of air - 'vital' and 'dead' air. Oxygen and nitrogen were still great novelties. Therefore no one, not even Cavendish himself, paid much attention to the tiny bubble of gas which was so different from nitrogen.

But why had chemists during the whole following century failed to observe that the nitrogen of the air is a mixture of two gases? They had analysed air thousands of times. Every student or laboratory assistant, even unskilled workers in a chemical plant, could do that. Chemists had calculated down to a hundredth of one per cent how much oxygen and how much nitrogen there was in the air. They had also established the fact that air contains .03% of carbonic acid gas. They had even discovered a minute portion of hydrogen in the air, less than one ten-thousandth of one per cent of it.

What is this 1%?

One ten-thousandth of one per cent! And here they had failed all these years to find a whole per cent of an unknown gas. Why?

Because this gas was invisible, tasteless, odourless. It did not reveal its presence in any way. A demure gas, it accompanied nitrogen everywhere without attracting any attention to itself, as if it had no existence of its own at all.

This new element refused to combine with any of the other elements. It stood aloof in the midst of all other things in the world that were continually changing, continually undergoing different chemical transformations.

A hermit element. A lonely element.

The new gas proved to be absolutely immune to every kind of chemical reaction. It was absolutely inactive, inert. So they gave it the name of argon, which in Greek means inactive, inert.

Ramsay tried mixing it with all the most active agents - with chlorine, a suffocating gas which corrodes metals, which takes the colour out of paint and rots cloth and paper. But it did not have the slightest effect on argon.

He tried to burn phosphorus in it. This poisonous stuff eats the hands, and unites with oxygen, burns of itself when exposed to the air. Argon was absolutely indifferent to it.

Neither heat, nor cold, nor electricity, nor strong acids could make argon participate in any chemical reaction. Everything jumped off it without having made any impression on it at all.

Ramsay and other chemists found it hard to reconcile themselves to the existence of so strange a substance, totally indifferent to everything else in the world.

It must combine with something! Why even the 'noble' metals, gold and platinum, which will not rust either in water or air and cannot be dissolved even in acids, nevertheless form compounds with certain substances. Is it possible that argon is the most unapproachable thing in the world?

Again and again Ramsay and his co-workers introduced reagents into vessels containing argon. They tried almost all the simple and many of the complex substances as the days, weeks and months sped by.

But it was no use - argon did not submit.

Rayleigh's apparatus for the preparation of Argon.

7. Gas from a mineral

One day after he had delivered a lecture at the Royal Society about his experiments with argon, Ramsay received a letter from a geologist, Henry A. Miers, who had not been present at the lecture but had evidently heard about it.

"I don't know whether you have tried combining argon with uranium or not," he wrote. "If not, I think it would be worth trying. A few years ago an American geologist named Hillebrand noticed that the uranium metal of cleveite, if heated in sulphuric acid, gives off a great amount of gas. Hillebrand said this gas was nitrogen. Perhaps it also contains argon? It seems to me it would be worth while to investigate in order to find if, possibly, some compound of uranium with argon

Ramsay's assistants were able to secure two ounces of cleveite for 18 shillings.

enters into the composition of cleveite."

Ramsay thought this a good lead. But where was he to get the cleveite? It is a very rare, expensive mineral, found only in Norway. On the chance that they might find some, one of Ramsay's assistants went hunting through all the London shops for a piece of cleveite and fortunately he was able to secure two ounces, about 60 grams, for 18 shillings, from a dealer in minerals.

The assistant immediately dropped the cleveite into sulphuric acid and heated it. It foamed and gave off a gas. But Ramsay, who was busy with some other experiments at the time, did not continue the experiment just then. He ordered that the gas be put away in a sealed container.

A month and a half passed, during which time Ramsay had made a number of other unsuccessful attempts to get argon to form a chemical compound with something else. He finally lost patience. He was helpless in the face of this super-stubborn, amazingly inert stuff. But before giving up he decided to make one last attempt with the gas formed by cleveite.

First he must determine whether or not this gas was nitrogen, as Hillebrand had stated, or argon.

Ramsay's assistant heated bits of magnesium red hot and passed the gas through this. If it was nitrogen it would find itself trapped and would be absorbed.

The gas came out almost untouched. That is, Hillebrand was wrong.

Next Ramsay went into the dark room of the laboratory to see what kind of spectrum this gas gave. He took a glass tube with metal plates - electrodes - fused to the ends and pumped the air out of it. Then he introduced the new gas and switched on the electricity. The gas in the tube became luminous at once.

Ramsay looked into the spectroscope.

He saw a number of bright lines of different colours, among them one very bright yellow line.

"Sodium," he thought. Apparently there was some sodium in the magnesium chips. "You can never guard against that."

In order to help himself understand this complicated spectrum, Ramsay filled another tube with pure argon and passed an electric current through it. Now in the spectroscope he got spectra from both of the tubes and could compare them.

Many lines in the two coincided. There was a yellow line in the argon spectrum too, but weaker. Evidently there was a smaller quantity of the always-present sodium in the second tube.

But for some reason the yellow sodium line of the second, or control, tube stood just a little bit to one side of the yellow line of cleveite.

Ramsay adjusted the spectroscope and gave the collimator tube with the slit a turn so that the lines would coincide. But the lines remained where they were. They stood close together but still they did not coincide.

"There's something wrong with our spectroscope," said Ramsay.

He turned on the light, took the spectroscope apart and carefully wiped off the lenses. But it did not help matters a bit. When he set the spectroscope up and looked in it again he saw once more that the sodium lines from the two tubes were out of line with each other.

What a nuisance! From the days of Bunsen and Kirchhoff every chemist and physicist had known that the sodium line has a definite place in the spectrum. If you should get a thousand samples of sodium from all over the globe and examine them they would all emit exactly the same yellow rays and give the same line in the spectroscope. Why then, here in this laboratory in the University of London, did the lines of sodium shift over?

Ramsay sat for a few moments at the spectroscope, his eyes fixed on the gas-filled tube, glowing with a cold, golden light. To tell the truth he did not find it hard to explain the phenomenon. Only he was afraid of the explanation which had occurred to him, afraid it might be too bold an assumption. He was afraid to trust his own luck.

"But why not suppose there is something else in this tube besides argon? Some other new, unfamiliar element!"

And like a flash there came into his mind a name for it - krypton - the Greek word for hidden, mysterious.

Ramsay immediately set about testing his theory. He worked many hours in that dark room, oblivious of time and indifferent to weariness. He examined the spectrum of the gas from cleveite, comparing it with the spectra of argon, nitrogen and sodium. But his rather poor spectroscope was not equal to so complex a piece of work. So he decided to appeal to his colleague, the physicist Crookes, who was a great specialist in the use of the spectroscope.

He sent Crookes a tube of krypton and asked him to examine it. This was the evening of March 22, 1895. Next morning a messenger boy came to the laboratory and Ramsay was called out of the dark room to receive the following telegram: Krypton is helium, Come and see for yourself, Signed Crookes.

Ramsay went and saw for himself; the yellow line of the cleveite gas coincided exactly with the mysterious line of the solar spectrum, the helium line.

Thus was the sun element found on earth.

8. Helium on Earth

How twisted and tangled the path to the discovery of helium was!

First astronomers suspected the existence of an unknown element in the sun.

Then Rayleigh, without any idea whatsoever about the make-up of the sun, began to weigh different gases - hydrogen, oxygen, nitrogen, in connection with the proof of some old scientific hypothesis.

All he wanted was to know as accurately as possible how much a litre of each of these gases weighed - nothing more.

Thanks to Rayleigh's experiments a long-forgotten experiment of Cavendish's was resurrected. And finally, through the combined effort of both Rayleigh and Ramsay, a heavy impurity was found in the air, a strange gas - argon.

Still with no idea of sun substance, Ramsay began to study the characteristics of argon and discovered that it was unusually passive, indifferent to all other substances.

When the geologist Miers put him on the trail of cleveite Ramsay hoped only that here he might at last find something that would combine with argon. He had no other idea in mind.

He got a gas from cleveite with which Hillebrand had worked a few years earlier without suspecting anything. Ramsay saw that this gas was neither argon nor nitrogen, but he did not at once realise what it was.

It was the physicist Crookes who first perceived that the new gas was that element which astronomers had discovered in the sun twenty-seven years earlier.

Ordinary earth-dwellers now held in their hands this guest from the far away luminary. They examined it, experimented with it, studied it from every angle. What marvellous properties would it disclose?

Many people, dazzled by the amazing story of its discovery, secretly expected it would turn out to be something quite extraordinary, quite unlike anything ever seen on earth before.

Sir William Crookes
(1832 - 1919)

But nothing miraculous happened. It was soon discovered that helium was a 'noble' gas, like argon - colourless, transparent, odourless and tasteless. It displayed the same stubborn unwillingness as argon to enter into any kind of chemical combination.

But in one respect it was totally unlike argon: in its weight. Helium proved to be one of the lightest substances in the world, coming next to hydrogen in lightness.

9. New discoveries

The great discoveries of those days threatened to shake the harmonious structure Mendeleev had reared twenty-five years before.

Ramsay could challenge Mendeleev. He could assert, with reason, that his system was no good, for there was no blank place on the Mendeleev table for the new elements. There was no group into which argon and helium could be put.

When they tried to squeeze them into the completed series of other elements, whose atomic weights conformed with theirs, it ruined the order of the whole table and then everything was thrown into confusion.

Some chemists, trying to find a way out of the uncomfortable situation, argued that argon and helium were not new elements at all.

"They are merely other forms of nitrogen," they said. "We know that other elements, too, have several forms. Carbon, for instance, exists in three forms: carbon, graphite and diamonds. Oxygen has two forms. Why not suppose that nitrogen has several different forms, too?"

But Ramsay had another idea on the subject.

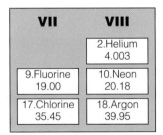

VII	VIII
	2.Helium 4.003
9.Fluorine 19.00	10.Neon 20.18
17.Chlorine 35.45	18.Argon 39.95

"We haven't discovered everything yet," he said. "We must keep on looking because there are apparently other elements similar to argon and helium. All together they will form a new 'family' of elements, a new series which will fit into Mendeleev's table. The new elements will not upset the periodic system. On the contrary, it will be more complete and consequently more accurate and correct."

So he and his co-workers set out to find the new elements, the 'relatives' of argon and helium.

He examined 150 rare minerals, 20 different mineral waters and even looked for traces of new elements in fragments of meteors.

And in the end he found them, but in an entirely different place - in the air.

VII	VIII
	2.Helium 4.003
9.Fluorine 19.00	10.Neon 20.18
17.Chlorine 35.45	18.Argon 39.95
35.Bromine 79.92	36.Krypton 83.80
53.Iodine 126.92	54.Xenon 131.30

Ramsay discovered that ordinary air contained three more elements besides argon. He named them neon, krypton and xenon. He had previously found helium in air.

These five similar elements fitted beautifully into the Mendeleev table, forming a new series, and thus putting the final touch to the proof of the correctness of Mendeleev's law.

Why was it Ramsay did not find all these elements at the same time, instead of discovering only argon at first?

Because there is a considerable amount of argon in the air, one litre out of a hundred, whereas there is very little helium, neon, krypton and xenon. Every time we draw a breath we take in about five cubic centimetres of argon, that is about half a tablespoonful. One five-thousandth would be helium, one ten-thousandth krypton and one one-hundred-thousandth xenon.

Of course all these gases pass through our lungs without having any effect on them whatever, since they are indifferent to every kind of matter and will not enter into any chemical changes.

Since their discovery, useful, practical application of all these rare gases has been found. Electric lamps are filled with argon to keep the incandescent filaments from burning out too fast. In this inert, lifeless gas not even inflammable oil will burn, let alone a metal with a high melting point.

Krypton and xenon are still better for this purpose. Lamps filled with them might almost be called perpetual, they last so long.

Neon is also used for electric illumination. But in this case ordinary bulbs are not used. You have seen the gleaming red tubes in thousands of signs in every city and town in the country. These tubes are filled with neon and when an electric current is passed through them the gas glows with a beautiful red light.

And light helium is wonderful for airships. Airships and strato-balloons filled with helium float in the air. True, helium is more expensive and slightly heavier than hydrogen gas, which is also used for this purpose; but hydrogen gas is combustible. One spark and the whole big airship will go up in flames like a torch. When helium is used there is no danger of fire. You could not light a fire in helium or argon if you tried; not even if you collected all the most inflammable substances in the world.

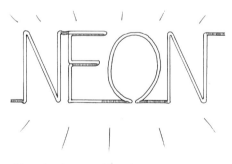

Neon is also used for electric illumination

10. Can an element be split up?

After the discovery of argon and helium many scientists believed that all the secrets of matter had been revealed. The Mendeleev table was almost filled. Most of the elements had been found. The reactions of hundreds of thousands of different combinations had been thoroughly explored. It seemed that now little remained to be discovered.

One hundred years earlier, at the close of the 18th century, Scheele, Lavoisier and other investigators had only just begun to ask what things are made of. And now every chemist could give a reasonably full and accurate answer to this question:

"About 80 elements," they would say. "These form the basic structure of the whole universe: the stars and the sun, the earth and its inhabitants, the rocks and the vegetation - all are made of these elements which chemists have so thoroughly explored. No matter what we split up into its parts, we always find the same ultimate components - elements. In one compound there may be two elements. In others, three, five or ten. But always and everywhere the elements are the same. Whether it be a meteor that has come from outside our world, or a human body, or a precious stone, or the ordinary dirt on the street, you will find that it is made of these 80 elements."

And the elements themselves - can they be split up into something simpler still?

"No!" scientists at the close of the 19th century would have answered emphatically. "There is nothing simpler than an element. This is the limit to the simplification of matter. Neither in nature nor in the laboratory nor in factories - nowhere and never has anyone seen an element split up into still simpler parts."

"Only compound things can change, go to pieces, disappear. Elements do not disappear. They are indestructible, they do not disintegrate and they cannot change into other elements. They are everlasting and unchangeable. There is just the same amount of iron and lead and helium in the world to-day as there was a hundred years ago or will be a hundred years from now; because not the tiniest atom of elemental matter can disappear or change."

"Every element consists of identical atoms. An atom is indivisible. It is the smallest particle of matter. Atoms of different elements can unite in various ways. But an atom of oxygen is the same whether it enters into the composition of the human brain, or ashes, or ore, or sea water or a thundercloud. It can travel all over the world, take part in an infinite number of chemical transformations, but it can neither disappear nor change; because the atoms of elements are eternal and unchangeable."

There is nothing simpler than an element.

That was what the science of chemistry taught at the end of the 19th century.

It was a very logical, very plausible doctrine. All the famous explorers of the elements about whom you have been reading, believed it.

But now you are going to read about some later discoveries which turned the whole structure of this theory topsy-turvy.

CHAPTER 6
Invisible Rays

1. Wilhelm Röntgen's discovery

At the very beginning of the year 1896, universities and academies were startled by a sensational announcement: a little-known German professor, Wilhelm Konrad Röntgen, had discovered certain new rays with the most remarkable characteristics.

They were invisible to the human eye, but they acted on a photographic plate and made it possible to take pictures in total darkness.

Also they made their presence known in another way. If a paper or glass screen, covered with a special chemical, was placed in their path, the screen would produce a bright phosphorescent glow.

But the most amazing thing of all was that the new rays passed, more or less easily, through any sort of object, just as light passes through glass. They penetrated tightly-closed doors, solid partitions, clothes and human flesh.

If, for example, a person held his wrist between the source of the rays and the screen, there would appear on the screen the shadow of a skeleton hand with moving fingers!

Dignified people in tightly-buttoned frock coats and starched cuffs could see their ribs and spinal column, the shadow of their whole skeleton on the screen. They could also see the watch in their waistcoat pockets and the money in purses tucked away in their trouser pockets.

People at once began to put the new rays to practical use. In America, for example, a physician used these rays to find out where a bullet had lodged in the body of one of his patients, only four days after he learned of the discovery of the rays.

But physicists were even more interested in Röntgen's discovery than doctors. They wanted to know what kind of rays they were, whether they were similar in nature to ordinary light rays or not, where they originated and why.

The story of how Röntgen made his discovery travelled from mouth to mouth.

He had been carrying on investigations of the phenomena that take place in a Crookes tube. The Crookes tube is made of glass with all the air pumped out and metal electrodes fused inside at both ends. When the current is turned on it produces an electric discharge in the rarefied air between the two electrodes and this causes the air and the sides of the tube to glow with a cold light.

Wilhelm Konrad Röntgen
(1845 - 1923)

Röntgen, quite accidentally, had left a package of unexposed photographic plates wrapped in black paper not far from a Crookes tube. Later, when he took them out to use them, he found they were fogged as though they had been exposed to light. This happened over and over again - new, absolutely untouched plates, tightly wrapped in black paper, were inevitably ruined if they were left lying near the Crookes tube.

Crookes himself and others working with discharge tubes had had this experience too, but had paid no attention to it. The plates were fogged if left near the tube - well, then keep them further away from it, they thought. But that did not satisfy Röntgen. He began experimenting to see what caused this trouble.

One day he was working with a Crookes tube covered with black cardboard. He was about to leave the laboratory and had put out the light when he happened to remember that he had forgotten to switch off the induction coil attached to the Crookes tube. Without turning on the light he went back to the table to turn off the switch. As he did so he noticed a faint, cold glow on a neighbouring table.

The light was coming from a spot where a sheet of paper covered with barium platino-cyanide was lying. This chemical has the property of giving off a cold phosphorescent glow under a strong light.

But there was no light in the laboratory! The weak, cold light of the Crookes tube could not cause this phosphorescence. Besides, the tube was covered with black cardboard. What had caused the phosphorescent screen to light up in the dark?

Later, when Röntgen was asked what he thought when he noticed this light, he replied:

"What did I think? I didn't think; I began to experiment."

He experimented, skillfully and persistently. He kept on seeking an explanation of the phenomenon and finally discovered the new rays.

Röntgen modestly called them X-rays to indicate that he did not himself know exactly what their real nature was.

Dozens of his fellow scientists in various countries hurried to complete the work Röntgen had started. Scientific journals were filled with accounts of experiments with X-rays - about their properties and their origin. Some scientists, in the heat of their excitement, thought they had discovered some more new rays. There were all kinds of reports of 'Z-rays' and 'black light'. 'Ray fever' raged in all the laboratories of both Europe and America.

2. A lucky mistake

Henri Poincaré, a French scientist, made an interesting guess about X-rays. When Poincaré read the account of Röntgen's discovery, one detail particularly struck him. Röntgen said that the X-ray originated at the part of the Crookes tube which was bombarded by electrified particles coming from the negative electrode, the cathode, and rushing towards the positive electrode, the anode. At this point in the glass wall tube, the phosphorescent glow was especially bright.

"Röntgen's rays originate at the point where there is intense phosphorescence." Poincaré reasoned. "Perhaps all phosphorescent bodies, not only Crookes tubes, emit these rays when an electric current is passed through them."

Charles Henri, a fellow countryman of Poincaré, at once set about testing this hypothesis.

Cold light may be produced in many different ways. People had long known of substances which give off a cold light if they are exposed to sunlight or any other strong light. Some of these substances continue to glow even after the original light is extinguished. Others will continue to glow for a short time only. Such materials as these are used for painting the figures on watch faces so that one can see what time it is at night without turning on a light.

Rotting wood also gives off a cold light. Combustible phosphorus glows with a greenish hue because it is slowly oxidising in the air. So, you see, there are many different causes of phosphorescence.

Poincaré suggested that whenever there was phosphorescence, from whatever source, Röntgen rays would always be emitted.

To test Poincaré's theory Charles Henri took zinc sulphide which is markedly phosphorescent in sunlight.

His experiment was very simple: he wrapped an ordinary photographic plate in black paper, laid a piece of zinc sulphide on top of the paper and exposed it to the sun. Then he took it into a dark room and developed the plate. There was a dark shadow on the plate under the spot where the phosphorescent substance had lain.

Did that prove Poincaré's theory correct? That every phosphorescent substance emitted invisible X-rays which passed freely through black paper?

That, at least, was the conclusion Henri came to and he reported it at the meeting of the French Academy of Sciences on 10th February, 1896. And a week later another Frenchman, Nevenglovski, made a report fully confirming Henri's theory. Nevenglovski had used calcium sulphide instead of zinc sulphide and had got the same results.

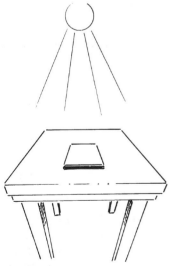

Charles Henri wrapped an ordinary photographic plate in black paper, laid a piece of zinc sulphide on top of the paper and exposed it to the sun.

From now on there was no meeting of the French Academy of Sciences at which someone did not report on the production of Röntgen rays by using phosphorescent substances.

It was an easy experiment to perform. It did not take long to wrap up a photographic plate in black paper, put a piece of some substance on it, lay it in the sun for a while and then develop the plate. Physicists hurried to try this experiment for fear someone else would get ahead of them.

X-rays now lost much of their former mystery. Why, even the phosphorescent figures on an ordinary watch face emitted them!

"You don't need any discharge tubes, which are so easily broken," said Trost, a member of the French Academy of Sciences. "You don't need any complicated and expensive electrical apparatus. Just put a piece of any phosphorescent material in a strong light and it immediately begins to give off X-rays."

But he was mistaken. They were all terribly mistaken - Trost and Henri and Nevenglovski. Fortunately, this mistake performed a valuable service for science and mankind, and we may all be very grateful to those scientists for the over-zealous haste and carelessness they showed in this instance.

3. When clouds hid the sun

When clouds hid the sun.

Henri Becquerel, a physicist, also joined in this hunt for X-rays. He experimented with several different phosphorescent substances and it seemed to him that, when exposed to a strong light, they all did give off invisible X-rays which acted on a photographic plate.

But he was not entirely satisfied with the indistinct black shadows he saw on the developed plates. So he decided to try further experiments with more powerful phosphorescent substances. They would, he thought, give off more powerful X-rays, and the imprint on the photographic plate would come out more distinctly.

Becquerel came of a family of scientists. His father made a special study of phosphorescence, and had investigated a very phosphorescent substance, the sulphuric acid salt of uranium and potassium. Becquerel, the son, had also made investigations of this salt at a later date. So he now decided to use it in his X-ray experiments. He also used other luminous substances containing uranium.

He got the results he was aiming for. The uranium salts, after exposure to sunlight, actually did make distinct photographic prints through black paper.

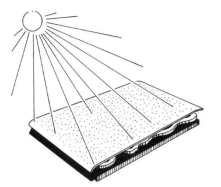

Then he exposed the whole experiment to the sun.

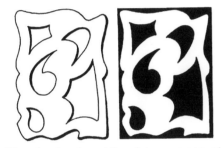

When he developed the plate, sure enough the pattern came out in white on a black background.

Becquerel's method was to wrap the plate in very thick black paper. On top of the paper he laid a pattern cut out of metal, and over the metal he laid a piece of thin paper and sprinkled a layer of uranium salt on this paper. Then he exposed the whole experiment to the sun.

When he developed the plate, sure enough the pattern came out in white on a black background. It was evident that the rays emitted by the phosphorescent uranium salt, invisible X-rays, penetrated the black paper but could not penetrate the metal, so the plate remained white where it was protected by the metal. Becquerel reported this to the Academy of Sciences.

Then one day, 2nd March, 1896, Becquerel appeared at the Academy of Sciences with a strange piece of news. Four days previously, 26th February, he had got everything ready for his regular experiment with uranium salt. The plates wrapped in black paper, the metal cut-out pattern, the salt crystals on top of it all. But that day clouds kept shutting out the sun, so he decided to put everything away in a drawer just as it was. He did not even remove the crystals of salt, so that the next clear day it would be easy to go ahead with his experiment.

Next day, the 27th, the sun did not come out at all, nor on the two following days.

On 1st March, he decided to develop the plate anyway. Since it had been shut up in the drawer most of the time, having had only a little weak sunlight on the first day for a brief period, he expected there would be little if any phosphorescence and, consequently, very few rays. He imagined there would be hardly anything to see on the plate.

But it turned out to be exactly the opposite. Never before in all his experiments with phosphorescent salts had he obtained so sharp an outline of the white pattern on the black background.

It was incomprehensible, inexplicable.

The more Becquerel experimented the less he understood what was happening. He found that the uranium salt was just as effective, and acted on the photographic plate through the black paper just as well, when it was not exposed to light as after exposure to a strong light.

He tried hiding bits of the salt in a box, then putting the box away in a drawer and leaving the drawer closed for fifteen days in a dark room. There could be no question of phosphorescence here. Yet the salt acted on the photographic plate just the same.

That meant that it kept on giving out even in inky darkness, the invisible rays which penetrated the black paper.

Becquerel next tried a kind of uranium salt which is not phosphorescent, on which the most brilliant light has no effect. It darkened the photographic plate just as well as did the phosphorescent kind.

4. Uranium the cause of it all

Doubts began to torture Becquerel. Maybe Poincaré was mistaken and phosphorescence had nothing at all to do with the invisible rays. Maybe uranium was the sole cause, for there was uranium in all the salts which gave such fine prints on the photographic plate. Did the invisible rays come from it?

How then explain Henri's and Nevenglovski's and Trost's experiments? How explain Becquerel's own earlier experiments before he began to use uranium salt? Didn't those phosphorescent substances also emit invisible rays? Didn't they also act through black paper on photographic plates?

A difficult knot to untie!

For a time Becquerel abandoned the use of uranium salts and again experimented with zinc sulphide and calcium sulphide, the phosphorescent substances with which he had begun to work a month before.

Wrapping several plates in black paper he laid a piece of some phosphorescent material on each one and exposed all of them to the sun at the same time. Then he developed the plates.

Not a single sign of a black spot on any of them!

He immediately repeated the experiment. The same thing happened again - the plates were perfectly blank.

Then he tried exposing his crystals to a strong artificial light instead of sunlight. He lit a bright magnesium flame over the plates and he also tried directing the blinding glare of an electric arc on to them. It did not help a bit.

To produce a more brilliant phosphorescence he heated some of the crystals and chilled others in salty ice. They did glow more brilliantly. Becquerel had never before seen so brilliant a phosphorescence. But it had no effect whatever on the plates.

He turned to Trost for help - Trost who had said that his phosphorescent crystals could take the place of the fragile Crookes tube, electric batteries, etc. The worthy member of the Academy was most willing to be of assistance - but, scandalous to relate, he too now got no results!

The same thing happened again - the plates were perfectly blank.

However, the uranium salt which had never had the property of phosphorescence and had lain in a dark drawer for a full month, continued to act on the plates through black paper with undiminished vigour.

Weeks, months went by. The uranium salt lay in a dark room and all the while kept emitting the invisible rays.

All the known chemical combinations of uranium were tried: oxides, acids and salts. They tried using it in the form of solid crystals, in powdered form, in liquid solutions, in molten form. Finally they tried the metal uranium in its pure form. All types of uranium, without exception, made imprints on a photographic plate. The pure uranium gave the most distinct imprint of all.

There could no longer be any kind of doubt about it: uranium and all its compounds emitted some kind of peculiar invisible rays, different from the Röntgen rays. And phosphorescence had nothing at all to do with it.

5. Another puzzle

Let us review the whole chain of events that led to the discovery of uranium rays.

Röntgen, working with a Crookes tube, discovered the invisible X-rays. These rays came from that part of the Crookes tube where the stream of electrified particles, passing through the rarefied atmosphere, struck the glass wall of the tube. At this point a marked phosphorescence was always observed.

Henri Poincaré advanced the theory that X-rays are emitted not only by a Crookes tube, but every time any kind of phosphorescence occurs.

Several investigators made hurried experiments and confirmed the theory that X-rays are actually emitted whenever phosphorescence occurs.

In his search for the most phosphorescent substance, Becquerel tried experiments with uranium salts. As a result he discovered that there was in reality no connection between phosphorescence and X-rays. But as a result of his experiments he discovered some new rays - uranium rays.

It is difficult to account for the fact that several different experimenters made the very same mistake. Was it, perhaps, that they were using imperfect photographic plates? Or that they were all badly developed? Or that the black paper was not entirely lightproof and the plates were slightly fogged by the bright sunlight without X-rays having anything to do with it? Or did the sulphurous phosphorescent substances when heated by the sun dissolve, and the volatile sulphurous gases

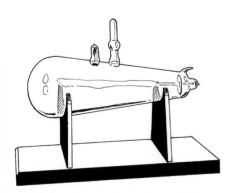

Röntgen's pear-shaped x-ray tube.

eat holes in the paper and let in some light to spoil the plates?

It is quite likely that all these causes had something to do with it. All kinds of accidents are likely to happen unless an experiment is planned and set up with the most painstaking care. And as a result the investigators get off on a wrong track.

That is exactly what happened in the cases of Charles Henri, Nevenglovski, Trost and, at first, Becquerel. But when he and Trost made more careful experiments it turned out that phosphorescent objects, unless they contain uranium, have absolutely no effect on photographic plates.

However, this was a very lucky mistake. Thanks to it, Becquerel discovered uranium rays, which later led to even more remarkable discoveries.

Uranium rays are in many ways much like X-rays. Both are invisible. Both have the property of acting on a photographic plate. Both types of rays electrify the air.

But uranium rays do not penetrate obstacles as X-rays do. They were able to pass through the thick black paper in which the plates were wrapped and through thin sheets of aluminium. They could not pass through the flesh of the human body, or through doors and thin walls, which Röntgen rays penetrated very readily.

The most interesting pictures could be taken with X-rays; and at first there was so much interest in them as a spectacle, that it became very popular to give public exhibitions with them. Röntgen rays were the rage. People would give evenings where the main entertainment consisted of installing Crookes tubes in their drawing-rooms and displaying their own skeletons to fashionable gatherings.

But the uranium rays were not so effective. Only specialists in physics knew about them. Actually, they were much more miraculous than X-rays.

X-rays were produced by the impact on the glass wall of a Crookes tube of electric particles, travelling at a high speed.

Uranium and its compounds emitted invisible rays spontaneously, without any visible cause. They did not require illumination by any kind of light; they did not have to be heated and no electric discharge had to be passed through them. Yet day and night, for months and years on end, they continued to give out some kind of rays, some kind of energy.

The emission of these rays never stopped for a moment. And the substances emitting the rays remained, apparently, entirely unchanged.

This was a genuine miracle - an amazing, inexplicable phenomenon.

Today we call this miracle radioactivity.

X-ray of a hand.

6. Mme. Curie's first experiments

Four years before the discovery of uranium rays, Marie Sklodowska had arrived in Paris from her native Warsaw. Her ambition was to become a scientist, a research worker.

Now it was difficult for a woman to get even a higher education in Poland in those days when it was still part of the old Russian Empire, to say nothing of going into serious scientific research. So Mlle. Sklodowska went to Paris.

Her life in Paris was a hard one. She earned her living by giving private lessons when she could get them, and when there were no lessons she worked at cleaning up the laboratory, washing the glassware and cleaning the apparatus in the university of Paris, the Sorbonne.

On her meagre earnings she could afford to rent only a tiny room on the sixth floor, right under the roof, and sometimes she was forced to live on nothing but dry bread for weeks at a time. In winter she had to carry coal up those five flights herself - when she was lucky enough to have money to buy coal. When she had no coal it was terribly cold in her little attic room. Water froze in the wash basin and the young student had to put on all the clothes she owned to keep from freezing.

But in spite of all these hardships Mlle. Sklodowska was a good student and soon completed her university course.

Not long after her graduation she married a French scientist, Pierre Curie, a professor of physics. When it was time to choose a subject for her independent research work she, with the advice of her husband, chose to study uranium rays.

This was unquestionably a difficult subject for a beginner. Almost nothing was known about uranium rays, as to their nature, the source of their energy, how they are produced in uranium compounds, or whether uranium alone had the power of emitting them.

Marie Sklodowska Curie plunged boldly into this labyrinth. First of all she had to learn to recognise uranium rays quickly and measure their intensity accurately. Working with photographic plates was too slow. Of course Mme. Curie could compare the different impressions made on photographic plates and judge by the density of the spots when the rays were more powerful and when weaker. But in this way she could not get any accurate measurements. A much better method was to measure the energy of the rays by means of some physical apparatus - just as temperature is measured by a thermometer, and the strength of an electric current by an ammeter.

Marie Curie
(1867 - 1934)

Pierre Curie
(1859 - 1906)

Her husband, Professor Curie, constructed an apparatus for her. He took an ordinary flat condenser - two metal plates separated by a layer of air. The lower plate was charged with electricity by a large storage battery; the upper plate was connected with the ground. So under ordinary conditions, air being, as you know, a non-conductor of electricity, the circuit was open.

But just as soon as a layer of uranium salt was sprinkled on the lower plate, the electricity immediately began to pass through the layer of air between the plates of the condenser. The uranium rays had made the air a conductor of electricity.

The more powerful the stream of rays, the better conductor the air became, and the heavier the current.

True, even with the most powerful radiation, the current was never more than a few billionths of an ampere. Nevertheless, it could be measured with a special instrument, also devised by Professor Curie.

The moment the substance they were using for an experiment was sprinkled on the lower plate of the condenser, the electrometer connected with the upper plate indicated whether or not uranium rays were being emitted. And their radiation could be measured with the greatest of accuracy.

Armed with this convenient instrument Mme. Curie set out at once to discover whether or not there were any other substances which spontaneously emitted invisible rays, as the uranium compounds did.

She assembled a quantity of minerals which she gathered wherever she could. From one laboratory she got chemically pure salts and oxides of all the known elements. Another gave her several rare salts, so rare that they were much more expensive than gold. A mineralogical museum sacrificed many samples of minerals gathered from the four corners of the earth.

She put all these on the lower plate of the condenser and carefully watched to see what the electrometer registered.

For a long time nothing happened. The indicator of the electrometer did not once change its position, although she had tried dozens of different compounds on the lower plate. But Mme. Curie kept on steadily testing one after another, always on the lookout for some signal from the electrometer. And finally one day the indicator did move away from zero.

A compound of the metal thorium was on the lower plate at that moment.

The first victory! That meant that uranium was not the only thing that gave off invisible rays. Thorium and its compounds also gave them off. And what about all the other things - compounds of iron, of lead, of magnesium, of carbon, of phosphorus? Did all the other countless substances in the world also have the property of emitting those rays? No, Curie's electrometer gave a definitely negative answer to this question.

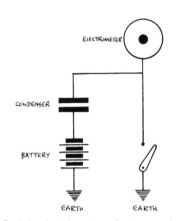

The Curie's electric set-up for measuring the intensity of radioactive radiation.

Then Mme. Curie went back to uranium compounds. She measured the ray-emitting ability of uranium oxides, of its salts, its acids, as well as all the minerals of which uranium is one of the component elements. They all electrified the air in different degrees - some more, some less, depending on the percentage of uranium they contained. The rays of a substance containing 50% uranium had only half the intensity of rays from pure, 100% uranium. One containing 25% had only one fourth; and so on.

This law held good without exception for all uranium compounds, all oxides, salts, acids and minerals containing uranium metal itself.

It was therefore obviously impossible that there could be any uranium compound with stronger radiation than that of pure uranium, since there could not possibly be a compound that contained more than 100% of uranium.

But two uranium minerals, pitchblende and chalcolite, acted in the strangest way when they were put on the lower plate of the condenser. They produced a much more powerful current than did pure uranium! How could this be?

Was it possible that there was some other ray-emitting element in these minerals? But what element? For uranium and thorium were supposed to be the only two elements that had the property of giving off rays. And the thorium rays were very little different from those of uranium.

In order to put this question to the test Mme. Curie decided to try making some chalcolite artificially. She made some out of chemical compounds in her own laboratory and the artificial product was identical in every respect with the natural chalcolite. It contained precisely the same percentage of uranium as the natural chalcolite.

And when she put some of this artificial chalcolite on the lower plate of the condenser the intensity of its radiation proved to be five and a half times less than that of the natural mineral.

That meant that there was some other active impurity in natural chalcolite and pitchblende - something superior to uranium, or possibly very much more powerful.

The situation took such a turn that Pierre Curie found it necessary to give up his own scientific investigations and take an active part in his wife's work.

7. Polonium and radium

The Curies tracked down this elusive something-or-other in a piece of pitchblende just as a hunter tracks down a rare animal in the wilderness.

They groped their way along with the help of Professor Curie's instrument. They used approximately the same method as Bunsen had used when he was trying to get the blue substance out of the Durkheim mineral water, except that Bunsen's clue was the blue rays of the spectrum, while all the Curies had to guide them were the invisible rays given off by the unknown substance.

Finally the day came when the Curies decided they had something to announce. Yes, it really existed, this something-or-other. They had got some of it. They gave it a name, although they had only a slight trace of it as yet, only a faint signal from the unknown substance. Step by step Pierre and Marie Curie separated this impurity from all the other elements that enter into the composition of pitchblende.

A simple example will explain to you how they proceeded. Suppose you were carrying a bag of salt along a sandy road and the bag had a hole in it and some of the salt spilled out and got mixed with the sand. How would you set about separating them again? You would throw the mixture into water and heat it. The sand would settle to the bottom. Then you would filter the solution through muslin and evaporate it and you would again have the pure salt without any admixture of sand.

Suppose you were carrying a bag of salt along a sandy road and the bag had a hole in it and some of the salt spilled out and got mixed with the sand.

A chemist does something like that when he has to isolate in pure form one single substance from a compound consisting of several substances, or from a mixture of such compounds. Only the chemist's method is much more involved and complicated.

He makes a solution of his compound, or mixture now in acid, now in alkali, now in water. In that way he gradually gets rid of the components one after another. What remains becomes constantly richer in the substance he wants to isolate. Finally the last impurity is driven off and what he has left is a chemically pure sample of the substance he is seeking.

This is the way Pierre and Marie Curie proceeded when they were trying to get a sample of the unknown substance from pitchblende. It was unbelievably difficult as there was apparently very little of it and they had no idea what its properties were. All they knew was that some unknown substance was evidently giving out powerful rays. And this was the clue they used to solve the mystery.

They dissolved the ore in acid and passed hydrogen sulphide through the solution. A dark precipitate of sulphurous metal salts settled out of the solution. All the lead which was originally in the ore, and also the copper, arsenic and bismuth settled out. Uranium, thorium, barium and other component parts of the ore remained in the solution. And what about the unknown substance? Had it united with those elements which had settled out or those which remained in solution?

The Curies placed both the precipitate and the solution on the condenser plate and found that the precipitate gave the most powerful rays. That indicated that the active substance was in the precipitate and must be looked for there.

As they gradually separated out the other substances, the Curies got a sample that gave out rays four hundred times as intense as those of uranium. In this sample there was a great deal of bismuth, a metal with which chemists are very familiar, and also an infinitesimal quantity of the unknown substance. Though they had not yet succeeded in isolating it completely from the bismuth, they now felt sure they would be able to do so in time.

In July 1898, Pierre and Marie Curie sent a report of their work to the French Academy of Sciences. They said they had discovered a new element, similar to bismuth, but having the property of emitting extraordinarily powerful invisible rays. If this should be confirmed, they wrote, they would like to have the new element named polonium, in honour of Marie Curie's homeland, Poland, the French word for which is Pologne.

Five months later the Academy heard another report by the Curies. This time they announced that they had discovered still another element in pitchblende, one which emitted even more powerful rays. This new element was very similar in its properties to the metal barium. They said they had already obtained some samples of it which gave out rays nine hundred times more powerful than those of pure uranium.

The Curies called this new ray-emitting element radium, from the Latin word radius, meaning ray.

8. A needle in a haystack

So Mme. Curie with the aid of her husband discovered two new chemical elements. Not a bad beginning for a young research worker!

But so far they had not yet succeeded in getting either of these elements in a pure form. They had only the most minute quantities in the form of impurities in bismuth and barium. They still had to isolate them in their pure forms. And this was no easy matter - something like trying to find a needle in a haystack.

It was not so hard to isolate the radium from the barium as the polonium from the bismuth. So the Curies decided to concentrate on radium. But they had only a small quantity of pitchblende ore to work with and in order to get any appreciable quantity of the new element, they needed at least a ton of ore. This cost money, and the Curies had no money. They were carrying on the experiments at their own expense. The government did not assist them at all.

They got their ore from Joachimstahl, in what was then Austria. At that place only the uranium was taken out of the ore and the rest was thrown away. It was precisely in this waste ore that the polonium and radium were to be found; so the Curies appealed to the Austrian Academy of Sciences, and the government of Austria with a magnanimous gesture consented to give these French scientists, absolutely free of cost, a whole ton of useless waste ore.

That gave the Curies enough material to work with. The next thing they needed was a place to treat it. In the yard of the school of Industrial Physics and Chemistry, where Professor Curie taught, there was an old tumble-down shed. The directors of the school graciously allowed the Curies to work in this shed.

For two years Mme. Curie remained there. Working heroically, it took her all that time to accomplish in her laboratory-shed what Bunsen had been able to do in six weeks in a big, well-equipped factory. She had no machines at her disposal, no factory vats and apparatus. All she had were glasses, flasks and bottles - and her own two hands. Nothing more.

For two years she dissolved the ore, evaporated it, precipitated crystals out of it, siphoned off the liquid, filtered the precipitates, dissolved it again, let it settle again, stirring the precious liquid with a metal rod for hours on end. She worked stubbornly, never hesitating to do the hardest jobs, with the enthusiasm of a person who knows she is working for a great end.

Her husband came to help her in his free time. Her baby, Irene, born a year before the discovery of radium, was brought to her here. She spent her entire life in this shed among bottles of distilled water and heaps of damp crystals. Many years later, in 1934, the year of Marie Curie's death, Irene Curie discovered artificial radioactivity, thus once again immortalising the name of Curie.

Bit by bit they separated out the unknown element from the ore. Soon they had samples whose radioactivity was five thousand times that of uranium. And the higher the proportion of radium in the mixture with barium, the greater became the radioactivity: ten thousand, fifty thousand, a hundred thousand times.... When they finally got an absolutely pure piece of radium it proved to have a radioactivity several million times that of uranium.

Out of the ton of uranium ore they got in all three-tenths of a gram of radium.

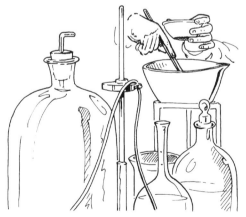

All Mme. Curie had were glasses, flasks and bottles - and her own two hands.

Out of the ton of uranium ore the Curies got in all three-tenths of a gram of radium.

9. A revolution in science

The rays emitted by radium were approximately the same kind of rays as those emitted by uranium. The difference consisted in their intensity. But this increase in intensity by millions of times completely changed the whole picture.

If someone should stroke your head gently with his hand, you would feel it as a caress. But multiply the pressure by millions and it would be enough to crush you flat as a pancake. That is what difference in quantity means.

Every tiny crystal of the radium preparation gave torrents of energy. It took hours to get an imprint on a photographic plate with uranium rays. Radium rays produced it instantaneously. Phosphorescent screens glowed brilliantly when exposed to these radium rays - as brilliantly as under Röntgen rays. Moreover, radium rays produced phosphorescence in things that had never before had the property of emitting a cold light.

The Curies used to notice in their shed at night how glass, paper, clothes, everything in the room that had been exposed to these powerful rays, would glow in the dark.

The crystals containing the radium gleamed so brightly one could read by their light. The rays also gave out heat - about 140 calories per hour per gram of radium. They also affected the human organism. Pierre Curie proved this by an experiment on himself. He exposed his hand to the invisible radium rays for several hours and as a result got a serious burn.

When the Curies first reported the properties of the new element, people were very sceptical. And was it any wonder? How could they conceive of the possibility of such an enormous quantity of light and heat and these tremendously powerful invisible rays coming from inside the radium without any conductor of energy whatsoever? Where did it all come from? Was it possible that the universal, unfailing law of the conservation of energy, did not hold good in that old shack in the yard of the Paris School of Physics?

This was too much to believe and contradicted all the experience of mankind for a century back.

Nevertheless, the fact remained that a few tiny bits of radium in the Paris laboratory of the Curies, by day and by night poured forth torrents of energy - energy out of nothing.

Out of nothing! That shook the foundations of science. Immediately dozens of experimenters all over the world began to work on radioactivity. In London, New York, Berlin, St. Petersburg, Montreal, Vienna, they studied these substances, trying to solve the riddle of the spontaneous emission of energy.

And in a short time many startling discoveries were announced.

It was discovered that radium emits three kinds of invisible rays: these are called by the first three letters of the Greek alphabet - alpha, beta and gamma rays. Gamma rays are like Röntgen rays, of the same nature as ordinary visible light rays, differing from them only in wave-length. But the alpha and beta rays consist of electrically charged particles of matter.

So radium not only emits energy from itself, but it destroys itself at the same time. True, the rate of destruction is so slow that in 1600 years only half of each gram of radium disappears; but that does not affect the principle. The important thing is that the matter of which this element is composed disintegrates and as it disintegrates it releases energy.

It was soon discovered that as radium decays it finally turns to lead and helium. But - helium is an element. And lead is an element. Then one element can be changed into another! What had been considered for centuries a naive dream, worthy only of the ignorant alchemists of the Middle Ages, had now become an incontestable scientific fact.

Many scientists, and educated people in general, refused to accept all this. It seemed to them that all the knowledge accumulated earlier would be useless if they acknowledged that the new discoveries were true. The matter which they had considered eternal turned out to be destructible. Elements which had been considered unchangeable down through the ages, did change from one to another. Atoms which were held to be indivisible and indestructible were split up into still smaller component particles of matter, alpha and beta particles, and these particles were charged with electricity.

It was enough to drive one crazy.

But progressive scientific people did not cling to old, outworn points of view. They marched boldly forward and on the ruins of the overturned theories they are now building a new science, more powerful, capable of explaining more fully all the transformations of matter and energy, and giving man more powerful tools with which to conquer the forces of nature.

Epilogue
1944 edition

I. Nechaev

10. And finally ...

Marie and Pierre Curie were the last of a long line of great element seekers.

True, a few rare elements have been discovered since polonium and radium, their neighbours in the periodic system. But these new discoveries have not brought about any startling changes.

Today the Mendeleev table may be considered quite complete. For the chemist of 1944 there are no more unknown elements in existence, not only on earth, but also in the entire universe. We know now that there are about 92 elements in all. Chemists, imitating and often surpassing nature, can create hundreds of thousands, even millions of the most varied and complex substances out of these few elements.

But for the science of our times the element has ceased to be the limit of divisibility. Since the great discovery of the Curies it has become clear that we may go farther - that we may split up the elements themselves.

Into what? Into the primitive form of matter - those minute particles of which the atoms of all the elements are built.

Do you remember how Mendeleev demonstrated that there was a common tie, a kinship among all the elements? At that time the reason for this kinship was not yet known. It is known now. The atoms of all elements - of light hydrogen, of lazy argon, of boisterous sodium, of noble gold, of radium - are all, every single one of them without exception, constructed of identical minute particles. We call these particles protons, electrons, alpha particles and neutrons.

Research workers of today can split off these primary particles from the atoms, can even make new combinations of them. So it has become possible to transmute one element into another artificially. Physicists make hydrogen out of atoms of nitrogen, carbon out of aluminium, gold out of mercury. True, they cannot yet make any great quantity of these artificial elements. Billionths of a gram is all they have been able to get in this way so far.

But this is only the beginning. The key to the mastery of matter is in our hands. And perhaps the day is not far off when we shall be able to take any common clay and make any kind of element - and all kinds of complicated substances too.

The achievements of the science of the future promise to surpass by far the achievements of the past.

There is no limit to man's mastery over nature - over matter and energy.

CHAPTER 7
The Story Continues

G.W.Jenkins

So many mysteries explained

When Nechaev completed his book in 1944, he bravely wrote in his postscript:

"For the chemist of 1944 there are no more known elements in existence, not only on the earth, but also in the entire universe. We know now that there are about 92 elements in all."

He was writing before the dramatic events of August 6th and August 9th 1945 when atomic bombs exploded over the cities of Hiroshima and Nagasaki. The secrecy surrounding the project and the research being done in the deserts of New Mexico was so great that no word had leaked out that four new elements had already been discovered: in 1940 elements 93, neptunium and 94, plutonium and in 1944, elements 95, Americum and 96, Curium. These elements were not so much discovered in the sense that the elements described by Nechaev were discovered, but were created artificially in an atomic reactor. The new and at the time, highly secret science of nuclear physics was able to create new elements for the first time by assembling the basic particles into new configurations. The first atomic bomb made use of an isotope of uranium, uranium 235 which was extracted from naturally occurring uranium but the second used plutonium, a new element specially created for the purpose.

This final chapter continues the story and brings it up to date. However, the most exciting part of the modern story is no longer about the discovery of new elements but of the discovery of the internal structure of the atom. This is not to say that no new elements have been found since 1944. Many have. At the time of writing in spring 1997, the total score has definitely reached 109 and may have reached 111. It is unlikely that either record will stand for long. Time will tell but in the meantime the truly fascinating story of the last fifty years is how the theory of quantum mechanics has succeeded in unravelling the secrets of the atom itself.

We now know, as Nechaev did not, why elements are so stable and yet are none the less capable of being transmuted or created. We also can understand at last why Mendeleev was correct to place the known elements into seven columns and why the discovery of the inert gases simply added an eighth column and did not upset the pattern. It is to these and other insights that this final chapter is devoted.

So many mysteries to explain

In the introduction overleaf, words such as 'isotope' and 'quantum' were used and the modern atomic number was given with each new element mentioned. Although such words are in common use nowadays and some readers will know what they mean, they were not employed by Nechaev in the earlier part of this book. Each new term will therefore be introduced as it is needed to advance the argument and the explanation of the astonishing developments and increased understanding gained in the last fifty years.

How small is an atom?

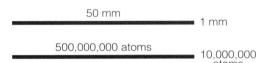

Nechaev knew that atoms were small and by 1944 their actual size was known. However, it is worth drawing attention to exactly how small they are. For example, consider the pair of printed lines on the left. Each is 50mm long and 1mm wide. The black ink used to print them is made by dispersing an element, pure carbon, in a solvent. When the solvent evaporates, the carbon atoms attach themselves to the molecules of the paper and the lines can be seen. Roughly speaking there are 10,000,000 atoms per millimetre. However, to print lines like these so that they can be seen, the layer cannot be just a single atom thick. In average printing, there needs to be at least 10,000 layers of atoms. If there were any less, the lines or indeed these actual words that you are reading, would look faded.

With this information, it is possible to calculate roughly how many carbon atoms are required just to make each of the lines.

$$5 \times 10^8 \times 1 \times 10^7 \times 1 \times 10^4 = 5 \times 10^{19} = 50,000,000,000,000,000,000 \text{ atoms}$$

If anyone needs convincing that atoms are very small indeed, then this calculation should do it!

What particles does an atom contain?

+ **Proton**
positive charge

Neutron
no charge

- **Electron**
negative charge

From the point of view of chemistry and the periodic table, it is sufficient to say that atoms are made up of three particles: protons, neutrons and electrons. Nuclear physicists know otherwise, but in considering the chemical properties of elements, particles such as mesons, positrons, neutrinos etc. can be safely ignored. Of the three particles we cannot ignore, protons have a positive charge, electrons have a negative charge and neutrons have no charge at all. It is a remarkable fact, so far unexplained, that the positive charge on the proton has precisely the same value as the negative charge on the electron and that the neutron is exactly neutral.

What is the structure of the atom?

This diagram illustrates a model of the atom which was proposed by Rutherford in 1911 and improved later by Niels Bohr. Although it is now known not to be correct in detail, it still remains a convenient one to use as a mental image of what an atom is like.

An atom divides naturally into two quite different regions. Firstly, at the centre, there is a dense nucleus which occupies about one ten thousandth of the diameter of the whole and contains the protons and neutrons. All the mass is concentrated there. Secondly there is a substantially empty region containing a whirling cloud of orbiting electrons. As will be shortly explained, atoms are considerably stranger than this diagram suggests but for the moment it serves as a very useful starting point.

Protons and neutrons have been found to be roughly equal in mass with the neutron very slightly heavier. Electrons are very much lighter. Since the mass of an electron is only about one 1840th of the mass of a proton or a neutron, it is normal practice to ignore the mass of the electrons altogether in chemistry calculations. Neutrons and protons are known jointly as nucleons and they determine what used to be called the atomic weight and is now called the atomic mass. The nucleus of hydrogen is a single proton and it is clear that the reason why so many elements are a whole number of times heavier than hydrogen is simply because the number of nucleons has to be a whole number.

Atomic numbers

It is the number of protons in its nucleus which determines which element an atom is. This number is known as the atomic number and for every proton in the nucleus there is an electron in orbit around it. Within all nuclei heavier than hydrogen, there are also some neutrons. The table below gives data for the first four elements of the periodic table.

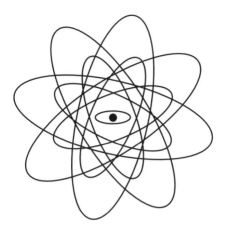

Atoms are considerably stranger than this diagram suggests, but it serves as a convenient mental image.

Masses of the fundamental particles

	Kg	Amu
Electron	9.1095×10^{-31}	0.00055
Proton	1.6726×10^{-27}	1.0073
Neutron	1.6749×10^{-27}	1.0087

Because the masses of these particles are so small when expressed in Kilograms(kg), it is normally convenient to express them in Atomic mass units (amu).
Carbon 12 is taken to be exactly 12 amu.

Element	Hydrogen	Helium	Lithium	Beryllium
Atomic Number	1	2	3	4
Electrons in orbit	1	2	3	4
Protons in the nucleus	1	2	3	4
Neutrons in the nucleus	0 or 1	1 or 2	3 or 4	5
Mass number (Total nucleons)	1 or 2	3 or 4	6 or7	9

Isotopes

With the exception of hydrogen with its single proton, all nuclei are a jumbling mass of protons and neutrons acting and reacting to two opposing forces. All nucleons are very strongly attracted to each other by what is known as the 'strong nuclear force' and the protons with their positive charges are also driven apart by the electrostatic force of repulsion. If the total forces of repulsion are greater than the forces of attraction, then the nucleus cannot hold together.

The electrostatic force of repulsion between pairs of protons is a hundred times weaker than the strong nuclear force of attraction but it is significant over larger distances. The situation is complex but it is a fact that only certain combinations of protons and neutrons are stable enough to survive for long. With any given number of protons there can be a range of different numbers of neutrons and these versions of the element are known as 'isotopes'. All isotopes of the same element are virtually indistinguishable in chemical reactions because it is the total charge rather than the mass which is most important in determining the chemistry.

Isotope	Protons	Neutrons	Electrons	Abundance
Silicon 28	14	14	14	92.21%
Silicon 29	14	15	14	4.70%
Silicon 30	14	16	14	3.09%

Although Silicon always has 14 protons and 14 electrons or it would not be silicon, there are stable isotopes with either 14, 15 or 16 neutrons. This gives mass numbers of 28, 29 and 30 corresponding to the total number of nucleons present. All these isotopes of silicon behave identically chemically and a normal sample of the element, as for instance when combined with oxygen (which also has three stable isotopes) in sand at the seaside, will contain all three types in fixed percentages.

For lighter elements, the ratio of neutrons and protons which give stable isotopes, tends to be about one to one but as the atomic number increases, so does the ratio. For instance, the stable forms of lead (82 protons) have 124, 125 and 126 neutrons.

$$^{206}_{82}Pb \qquad ^{207}_{82}Pb \qquad ^{208}_{82}Pb$$

$$^{28}_{14}Si \qquad ^{29}_{14}Si \qquad ^{30}_{14}Si$$

$$^{16}_{8}O \qquad ^{17}_{8}O \qquad ^{18}_{8}O$$

Each of the elements lead, silicon and oxygen has three stable isotopes.

A convenient way of writing the chemical formulae to distinguish between the stable isotopes of lead, silicon and oxygen is given in the panel. Each symbol shows the mass number and the atomic number. Strictly speaking, the chemical symbol is unnecessary. However few people can remember the atomic numbers of all the elements, so a reminder is helpful!

The relative atomic mass

The scientific community now uses a common standard to measure the mass of atoms and molecules. They are given relative to carbon12 (six protons, six neutrons and six electrons) which is taken to be exactly 12 units. Samples of most naturally occurring elements contain mixtures of different isotopes and if their relative abundances are known, then the relative atomic mass can be calculated. Silicon is a typical element in that most of it consists of a single isotope, silicon 28. The relative abundances of the three stable isotopes of silicon are given opposite. The relative atomic mass of a normal sample of silicon could be calculated thus.

$$28 \times 0.9221 + 29 \times 0.0470 + 30 \times 0.0309 = 28.11$$

This is an over-simplification as we should use the number of atomic mass units for each isotope and not the mass numbers but it shows how the calculation should be done. The published observed value for silicon is 28.0855 amu.

Silicon 28	27.97693
Silicon 29	28.97649
Silicon 30	29.97376

The precise values of the masses of the three stable isotopes of silicon in amu.

It is not possible to arrive at the mass of an isotope in atomic mass units by simply adding together the atomic mass units for the particles within it. The actual mass of an atom is always slightly less. This 'mass deficit' or 'mass defect' was explained by Einstein in terms of the energy which is released when forming the atom from its constituents through the famous relation $E = mc^2$. For instance, Helium 4 consists of two protons, two neutrons and four electrons, giving an apparent total mass of 4.0331 amu. However, the actual mass is 4.0026 amu, a 'defect' of 0.0305 amu.

The transmutation of elements

To change one element into another, you have to change the number of protons in the nucleus. This demands an enormous amount of energy, much more than any chemical reaction can supply. That is why elements seem so stable and why the dream of the ancient alchemists of being able to change lead or mercury into gold by discovering some cunning chemical mixture, process or potion is disappointingly impossible.

$$^{14}_{7}\text{N} + {}^{4}_{2}\text{He} = {}^{17}_{8}\text{O} + {}^{1}_{1}\text{H}$$

Although one element cannot transmute into another through a chemical reaction, it can do so by means of a nuclear reaction. The first clear demonstration that this was possible was given by Rutherford in 1919. He changed nitrogen (7 protons) into oxygen (8 protons) by bombarding it with helium nuclei. A helium nucleus contains two protons and two neutrons and the energy of the impacts was sufficient to rearrange the number of protons and neutrons between the nuclei. The equation for the reaction, showing the mass numbers and the atomic numbers is given on the left. Note how the total numbers of protons and neutrons are unchanged.

Radioactivity

When nuclei are unstable and spontaneously disintegrate, they are said to be 'radioactive'. The process of disintegration changes such elements and isotopes into others and also releases a great deal of energy. This energy is manifested in the form of radiation and heat. It was soon recognised that three different kinds of radiation were emitted by radioactive substances and at first they were classified as alpha, beta and gamma rays. They required different thicknesses of shielding materials to stop them and could be separated by how they reacted to magnetic fields. Further research showed that alpha rays were in fact fast moving helium nuclei, beta rays were energetic electrons and gamma rays were indeed rays. They were like X-rays but with shorter wavelength and greater penetrating power.

A radioactive element is one where all the isotopes are unstable. Other elements have some isotopes which are stable and some which are not. For instance, silicon has the three stable isotopes already discussed but it also has eight known isotopes which are unstable and therefore radioactive. Lead has no fewer than 28 known unstable isotopes. The largest stable nucleus is bismuth 83 with 209 nucleons in all. All the new elements discovered since 1944 are radioactive including a significant milestone passed in 1947. Element 61, promethium was made, filling the only gap which then remained in the first 92.

The unit of radioactive decay is the becquerel and it is equal to one nuclear disintegration per second. Since this is a very small unit, an alternative one is sometimes used, the curie, the radioactivity of one gram of radium 226. One curie is 3.7×10^{10} disintegrations per second. It is easy to see why the discovery, identification and separation of radium by the Curies was so astonishing. So much energy is released and it is so constant. In a darkened room, radium glows and continues to glow, emitting energy in a profligate and mysterious way. Over a few years the decline in activity is so slight as to be almost undetectable.

It is never possible to forecast when a particular atom will suddenly break up, but so many billions are present in even a small sample that the actual proportion which disintegrates in equal periods of time is remarkably constant. This rate is unaffected by heat, motion or chemical reactions.

Within the nucleus the protons and neutrons are in a continuous state of random motion. From time to time the nucleons become arranged in such a way that certain groups are able to break away from others. Having escaped from the attraction of the strong nuclear force, the electrostatic repulsion between the charges on the protons pushes such groups further away from each other so that they escape completely. This escape or 'splitting of the atom' is often violent and because the number of protons has changed, new elements are created.

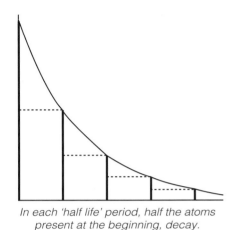

In each 'half life' period, half the atoms present at the beginning, decay.

Some half lives	
Uranium 238	4,500,000,000 years
Uranium 235	700,000,000 years
Carbon 14	5,730 years
Radium 226	1,620 years
Tritium (Hydrogen 3)	12 years
Radon 222	3.82 days
Bismuth 214	19.9 minutes
Nielsbohrium 262	0.007 seconds

One of the commonest groups to escape from radioactive atoms in this way is the alpha particle, a group of two protons and two neutrons. Once alpha particles have escaped, they may impinge on other atoms and cause other changes or simply acquire two electrons and become helium gas. In 1903, Ramsay and Soddy showed that helium was continuously produced by the decay of radium. Although helium was first discovered in the spectrum of the sun, it is present in substantial quantities in natural gas and is now commercially available for many purposes including ballooning and deep-sea diving. This helium, produced by the decay of naturally occurring radioactive elements deep within the earth, is trapped by the same rock formations which trap the methane and other petroleum gases.

Half-life

The way that instability is measured is by the length of time it takes half of the atoms to self-destruct. This is called the half-life. The shorter the half-life, the more active the material. The number of atoms present in a sample decays in an exponential fashion. The graph is always the same shape, but the time scale along the bottom can be very different for different substances, from millions of years down to tiny fractions of a second.

Different combinations of protons and neutrons (i.e. different elements and different isotopes) decay in different ways and produce different decay products. The detail is very complicated but each has a unique signature and produces widely different amounts of energy. The table shows the half-lives of a selection of elements with a remarkable spread of activity. At the head of the table is uranium 238 with a half-life of 4,500,000,000 years, roughly the age of the earth. About half of the atoms of uranium 238 present when the earth was formed have since decayed and the other half still remain. With such a long half-life and a relatively low rate of energy production, bars of the metal can be safely held in the hand.

Radium has a half-life of 1620 years and is very energetic indeed and a small sample will soon burn the skin.

Carbon 14 is produced in the upper atmosphere by the bombardment of nitrogen by neutrons from cosmic rays. While alive, plants and animals absorb it via carbon dioxide and so it is present in all living tissue. Fortunately as only a very small proportion of the total. Most organic carbon consists of the stable forms, carbon 12 (98.9%) and carbon 13 (1.1%). A one gram sample has therefore a very low activity. On death, the exchange with the atmosphere ceases and the carbon 14 present continues to decay. Its half life is 5,730 years and the steadily changing proportion present in a sample of organic material allows it to be dated. This technique has been immensely valuable in unravelling human history.

Chain reaction

In the table overleaf it may be thought remarkable that uranium 235, the fuel for the atomic bomb is almost as stable as uranium 238. It has a half life of 700,000,000 years. However, what made uranium 235 the choice for the bomb was not the way that it disintegrates spontaneously but what happens when it is hit by a free neutron. When an extra neutron is added to the nucleus then the nucleus splits into two roughly equal parts releasing two or three free neutrons and a huge amount of energy. If these extra neutrons enter another uranium 235 atom then it also splits and produces still more. This is known as a chain reaction and in a fraction of a second an enormous amount of energy is released. Neutrons do not easily interact with atoms and a high proportion are lost and absorbed into other materials. Thus a chain reaction takes place only when sufficient mass, known as the critical mass, of the reactive substance is present. The principle of an atomic bomb is simple enough. Two pieces, each below the critical mass are suddenly brought together around a neutron source. Once the reaction starts, the number of neutrons increases rapidly and uncontrollably. Virtually instantaneously, the explosion takes place.

In a nuclear power station the amount of fissile material is carefully controlled so that on average just one neutron is released for each neutron absorbed. The dream of unlimited and cheap power which nuclear energy appeared to offer is rather tarnished at present. The need for safety and control increases the costs greatly and the problem of what to do with the unwanted fission products has not yet been resolved. It will be for future generations to solve these problems. It is certain that if solutions are to be found, then it is likely to be through a greater understanding of the nature of the atom. It is now time to start to appreciate just how strange it is.

Both particles and waves

Through all the discussion of elements, isotopes and radioactivity, it has been convenient to regard electrons, neutrons and protons as tiny particles. However, quantum mechanics tells us that this is only one way of looking at them. They can also meaningfully be described as waves.

From the time of Newton there was a long debate about the nature of light. Some experiments seemed to suggest that it was 'corpuscular' or particle-like. Others seemed to suggest that it was a kind of wave. The debate raged for many years and was finally settled when it was realised that it was both. A similar debate took place over the electron. It is a curious fact that J.J.Thomson received a Nobel Prize for proving that an electron was a particle and his son G.P.Thomson received one for proving that it was a wave.

This dual wave-particle nature of matter is now established beyond doubt and is the heart of the quantum mechanics which has so revolutionised our understanding of the structure of the atom.

The French scientist, De Broglie showed how to calculate the wavelengths for particles of any size and proved that the greater the momentum (mass x velocity) of a particle, the shorter its wavelength. The shorter the wavelength, the more 'particle-like' it appears to be. We should therefore expect protons and neutrons to seem more like particles and electrons to seem more like waves. This is indeed how they behave and are generally regarded. However, we must never lose sight of the fact that all particles have this dual nature.

Orbits and orbitals

The word orbit is used to describe the path traced out by a planet around the sun or by a satellite or spacecraft around the earth. The mass of such objects is so great that their wave natures are unimportant and can be ignored. This means that a precise path can be calculated.

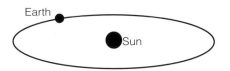

The word 'orbital' is used to describe a region of space where an electron might be found. It is customary to represent an orbital by a fuzzy diagram, because quantum mechanics does not tell us precisely where an electron is, but gives the probability of finding the electron in each region of the orbital. It is a probability statement and the darker the shading, the more likely it is that the electron will be found there.

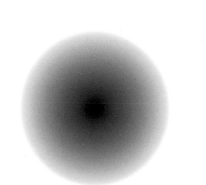

Of course this diagram is just a two dimensional representation of a three-dimensional orbital. Fuzzy as the diagram may be, do not think that there is anything fuzzy about the idea or vague about the results which can be calculated. The ideas of quantum mechanics allows us to explain the properties of atoms brilliantly.

The quantum

On a sub-atomic scale, energy levels are not continuous but 'packet-like'. A quantum is the name given to a packet of energy. Energy is added or taken from atomic systems exactly one quantum at a time. Because a quantum of energy is very small, this 'discreteness' is not apparent on a human scale any more than it is apparent in ordinary life that matter is made up of atoms and that atoms are mostly empty space. When light and other forms of electromagnetic energy are regarded as particles, they are called photons. A single photon is therefore a quantum of electromagnetic energy.

Quantum mechanics is the mathematical treatment of quanta and atomic structure. It is also known as 'wave mechanics'. It is true to say that the ideas are very subtle and can only really be understood and appreciated with the help of advanced mathematics. However, just as it is possible to make a great deal of use of a motor car with only a superficial knowledge of the parts and engineering which make it work, so one can understand quite a lot about elements and the nature of the periodic table without going too deeply into the actual mathematical reasoning behind quantum mechanics. What we do need, however, is an appreciation of the significance of some fundamental ideas such as 'energy levels' and what is meant by a 'quantum jump'.

Energy levels

This diagram shows a side view of some ordinary steps leading up from horizontal ground. It can serve as a useful mental model of the idea of energy levels within atoms. Let us imagine that someone has placed an apple on each of the three lowest steps and that these apples are identical. The energy in this situation is called 'potential energy' or 'gravitational energy'. Each horizontal tread represents a stable energy level, a place where an apple can remain until disturbed by some external force or event. Each of the three apples occupies a different energy level and it makes sense to number the steps 1, 2, 3, ... starting with the lowest. To raise an apple to a higher step or energy level requires work against the force of gravity. Similarly an apple falling to a lower step releases energy and this energy appears in the form of motion. The lowest apple is on the ground and cannot fall lower.

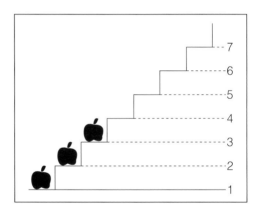

A diagram which can be used as a convenient mental image for the idea of energy levels within atoms.

We also talk of energy levels being 'occupied' or 'vacant'. In the example of the steps the three lower energy levels 1, 2 & 3 are occupied and the four higher energy levels 4, 5, 6 & 7 are vacant.

Within atoms there are also distinct energy levels or 'steps', although not because of the force of gravity. They are there because negative electrons are in the vicinity of a positively charged nucleus and are a consequence of the wave nature of the electron. The lowest energy level is known as the 'ground state' and it was a triumph of the theory of quantum mechanics to forecast both that there must be energy levels and also that a ground state must exist. These were very important ideas and were major factors leading to its acceptance. An electron, although negatively charged and attracted to the positively charged protons can never fall or spiral into the nucleus.

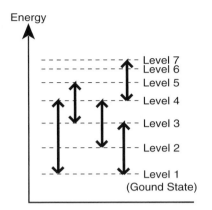

Energy

Level 7
Level 6
Level 5
Level 4
Level 3
Level 2
Level 1
(Gound State)

Electrons jump between energy levels when absorbing and emitting a quantum of energy.

Another way of representing the energy levels within the atom is to use a series of horizontal bars, here shown as dotted lines. Note how the intervals between the energy levels are not equal as they were in the 'stairs' example but become steadily closer together as the energy increases.

Since electrons can only exist at permitted energy levels and energy can only usually be absorbed or emitted one quantum at a time, they must jump between them. Each jump absorbs or emits a precise quantity of energy. This diagram shows some of the quantum jumps between energy levels which are available. The exact pattern of energy levels within a particular atom depends on the number of protons in the nucleus and since this number is unique for each element, so is the pattern of quantum jumps. When Bunsen and Kirchhoff discovered the line spectrum as a means of identifying elements, they were making use of the uniqueness of these patterns of quantum jumps or transitions.

Do not fall into the trap of supposing that all quanta have the same amount of energy. They do not. The energy of a photon is proportional to its frequency or inversely proportional to its wavelength.

Wavelength and frequency

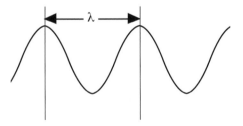

The wavelength is the distance between consecutive maxima.

The wavelength of light is usually expressed by the Greek letter λ(lamda) where λ is the distance from the crest of one wave to the next. Nowadays it is usually expressed in nanometres, one billionth of a metre. The wavelengths of light in the visible spectrum fall in the range of 680nm (red) to 400nm (violet).

The frequency of electromagnetic radiation, including visible light, is expressed by the Greek letter ν (nu). It is measured in Hertz (Hz) and is the number of waves which pass a fixed point in a second. The letter c is always used to represent the velocity of light and is of course a universal constant.

Since Wavelength x Frequency = Velocity of light the formula is $\lambda \times \nu = c$. With this formula, it is possible to calculate the wavelength of light of any colour from the frequency or the frequency from the wavelength.

The energy of photons

The formula for the energy of a photon is $E = h\nu$, so it is directly proportional to its frequency. The constant h is one of the fundamental constants of the universe. It is known as 'Planck's constant' and it has a very tiny value in m.k.s. units. This is why quantum mechanics is only important for microscopic happenings. Planck's constant sets the scale where quantum mechanical effects are important.

Energy per photon (10^{-24} J)	
Lower Frequency	
Radio Waves	(<0.1)
Infra Red	20
The Visible Spectrum	
Red	28
Orange	34
Yellow	34
Green	37
Blue	42
Indigo	45
Violet	47
Higher Frequency	
Ultra-Violet	60+
X-rays	5,000+

This table shows typical amounts of energy of photons of different frequencies in convenient units. It shows that a quantum of violet light (47 units) has nearly twice the energy of a quantum of red light (28 units). It also shows that a quantum of X-ray frequency contains more than a hundred times more energy than a quantum of visible light. A quantum of gamma radiation contains even more.

The spectrum

Most of us have seen what happens to sunlight when it passes through a prism and have admired the rainbow colours which are produced. It was Isaac Newton in 1666 who first experimented in this way and who discovered that white light was in fact a mixture of colours. Since different colours have different wavelengths, white light is a mixture of light of all wavelengths.

For quantum mechanics it is convenient to think in terms of photons and frequency so white light is a mixture of photons of different frequencies. A prism bends the paths of photons of different frequencies by different amounts and so is able to separate them. Red photons, those with the least energy, have their paths bent least and violet photons, those with the most energy, have their paths bent most. A prism is therefore able to sort photons by their frequency.

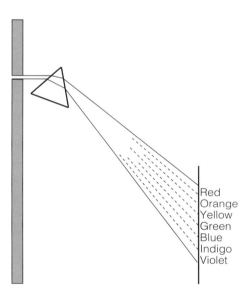

A prism sorts photons by their frequencies. Red photons have the lowest frequency and violet the highest.

The line spectrum

When an atom is heated in a flame or excited by an electric current the electrons jump between different permitted energy levels and emit and absorb a unique 'signature' of photon frequencies. If this emitted light is passed through a prism, the photons are sorted by frequency and the result is seen as a spectrum of coloured lines.

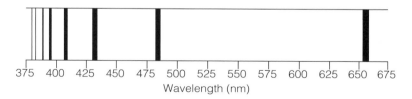

This is the pattern of lines in the visible spectrum (The Balmer Series), which appears when hydrogen is burnt or excited and the light is passed through a prism. Confidence in the power of quantum mechanics as a scientific theory was greatly enhanced by the fact that the calculated wavelengths agree precisely with those observed by experiment.

Spectroscopy

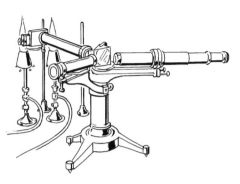

Kirchhoff's improved spectroscope

As was explained by Nechaev earlier in this book, it was Bunsen and Kirchhoff in 1859 who first used the line spectrum as a method of identifying elements. This method of analysis had the great advantage over earlier methods in that only minute quantities of the substance were required and the results could be obtained very quickly. The first element that they identified in this way was caesium which they named after the sky-blue colour of the principle photons that it emits. After discovering rubidium by using the dark red lines in its spectrum, they went on to identify no fewer than 30 elements in the sun. This was painstaking work as simply to confirm the presence of iron, more than 60 lines had to be checked and identified. Nowadays sensitive spectroscopes linked to computers are used to analyse almost instantly the spectra from distant stars and to identify the elements which are present. That is why it is reasonably certain that the rest of the universe contains only the same elements as are present on earth.

How do we see colour?

When white light falls upon atoms and molecules, some photons are reflected and some are absorbed. If the substance is opaque, then the photons are absorbed by layers near the surface. If it is transparent, then they are able to travel right through with only a small proportion being absorbed on the way. The energy contained in the photons manifests itself as heat, meaning that the atoms and molecules jostle each other just a little more.

A photon with the right amount of energy to match one of the allowed quantum jumps in a particular atom or molecule, will interact with it in a quite different way. The photon will cause an electron to leave a lower orbital and rise to an orbital with a higher energy level. This higher orbital is unstable and so the electron will almost instantaneously drop back to the lower level and emit a photon of that frequency or colour. The direction of emission is random and since photons will be absorbed and emitted millions of times every second, photons of that colour will go out in every direction. Objects are therefore absorbing and emitting photons of some frequencies, but absorbing only the photons of others. In our eyes there are three kinds of molecules, each able to interact with photons of a band of frequencies. In very crude terms one detects red photons, one green and the third blue, although there are overlaps. Our brains are able to process these interactions and we interpret each mixture as a colour. We are fantastically good at detecting and analysing mixtures of photons in this way and can distinguish perhaps ten million different colours. It is fascinating to realise that the colour we see all around us is the consequence of quantum jumps within atoms!

Not too real!

For some purposes it is convenient to regard a photon as a particle, a packet of energy, but it is unwise to think of it having too much of a separate existence. For instance, if a gas is excited by an electric current (a stream of electrons), it glows with a characteristic colour. For example, neon glows red and sodium yellow. The atoms continue to emit a stream of photons with certain frequencies as long as the current is applied and it is sensible to ask where do all these photons come from? It is not sensible to think that they were inside the atom, waiting to be ejected.

A good analogy is that it is rather like the words created when you speak. The words are not there in your vocal chords waiting to be released, but are created by their action when they are needed. Having been created, they carry the information through the air until eventually they are absorbed and disappear again.

Some words are recorded, or cause actions which change the world, but most simply appear and then disappear. So it is with photons. Some cause permanent chemical changes and assist in reactions. Some set off on journeys across space lasting millions of years but most are simply re-absorbed back into the general energy of jostling atoms and molecules.

Electron pairs

All attention has so far been concentrated on the behaviour of a single electron jumping between energy levels and naturally settling into the ground state when unexcited. Electrons are negatively charged and repel each other, so the next point to consider is where the electrons in a many-electron atom are to be found. One possibility is that all of them might settle into the ground state, the state with the lowest energy and only jump out of it when a photon of the correct energy arrives. This is not the case.

There is a law of nature, the Pauli Exclusion Principle, which states that two identical particles cannot share the same orbital. At first sight this might seem to suggest that each electron in a multi-electron atom must occupy its own orbital. However, electrons have a curious property called 'spin' which has two states and so an electron in one state is not identical to an electron in the other. This means that an orbital can be occupied by a maximum of two electrons, one in each state. When this happens they form an 'electron-pair'. Once any orbital is occupied by two electrons it is full and other electrons must go elsewhere. This requirement, together with the minimum energy rules, is the key to understanding the underlying patterns in the periodic table.

The minimum energy rules

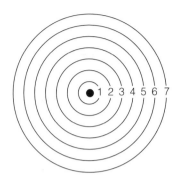

1. Electrons within an atom take up the configuration with the lowest possible energy when in an unexcited state.

2. Two electrons will share an orbital and form an electron-pair only when all other orbitals at that energy level are occupied.

Introducing shells

It is convenient to visualise energy levels as grouped together into a sequence of spherical shells surrounding the nucleus. Within the shells of ordinary atoms there are four different types of orbital and they are classified by the letters s, p, d and f. They always occur in this order and the numbers of available orbitals is the increasing sequence of odd numbers 1, 3, 5, 7. This is exactly as quantum mechanics predicts should happen. The reason for using these particular letters is simply that the early workers on spectroscopy did so, there is no other significance.

Shell	1	2	3	4	5	6	7
Orbitals available	1s (1)	2s 2p (1) (3)	3s 3p 3d (1) (3) (5)	4s 4p 4d 4f (1) (3) (5) (7)	5s 5p 5d 5f (1) (3) (5) (7)	6s 6p 6d (1) (3) (5)	7s (1)
Total Orbitals	1	4	9	16	16	9	1
Max. Electrons	2	8	18	32	32	18	2

The first shell includes orbitals of type s, the second of types s & p, the third of types s, p & d and so on, as shown in the table above. There is a satisfying pattern for the first four shells that the total number of orbitals available in successive shells is the square of the shell number. According to theory, the pattern would continue further, but in practice this takes us beyond the end of the real periodic table and so there is no point in continuing. Of those listed above, not all of the theoretical orbitals in shells 5, 6 & 7 are ever required in real atoms.

When a shell is full, the electrons are in a stable low-energy configuration and are not easily persuaded to take part in chemical reactions.

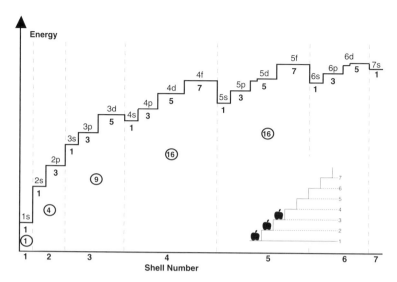

Building up to the periodic table

The idea of energy levels was introduced by means of seven ordinary steps and three apples. This diagram shows that although the situation inside a many-electron atom is more complicated, the basic idea is still the same. Each horizontal step represents an energy level and at each level there can be either 1, 3, 5 or 7 orbitals. Since each orbital can hold a maximum of 2 electrons, individual steps can hold up to 2, 6, 10 or 14 electrons The original seven steps were numbered 1 to 7 and they represent in a broad way the energy levels of the electron shells. However within all the shells except for the first, there are different energy levels associated with the orbital types of s, p, d & f. This means that the steps are in essence divided into sub-steps. Some of them even step downwards.

It is this diagram, entirely predicted by quantum mechanics, which illustrates both the structure and the detail of the periodic table.

When the elements are placed in the order of their atomic numbers, then each element has one more proton and one more electron than the previous one. Let us imagine the extra electron being 'fed into' the system. It will naturally seek out the orbital with the lowest energy which is available to it. In this way the electronic structure of successive elements can be regarded as filling up from the inside as the atomic number increases. Since we know that each orbital can take a maximum of two electrons, the whole periodic table can be built up in a logical fashion one element at a time starting with hydrogen. This process is known as the 'Building up Principle' or sometimes the 'Aufbau Principle' after the German word.

Orbital	Max Electrons	Element	Electronic Structure
1s	2	1. Hydrogen	1
		2. Helium	2
2s	2	3. Lithium	2.1
		4. Beryllium	2.2
2p	6	5. Boron	2.3
		6. Carbon	2.4
		7. Nitrogen	2.5
		8. Oxygen	2.6
		9. Fluorine	2.7
		10. Neon	2.8
3s	2	11. Sodium	2.8.1
		12. Magnesium	2.8.2
3p	6	13. Aluminium	2.8.3
		14. Silicon	2.8.4
		15. Phosphorus	2.8.5
		16. Sulphur	2.8.6
		17. Chlorine	2.8.7
		18. Argon	2.8.8

Filling the shells

This table shows the systematic way in which the orbitals fill up. Orbital 1s is the first to fill because it has the lowest energy of all. The single electron of hydrogen enters it and then the second electron of helium completes the electron-pair.

Element 3 is lithium with three electrons. Two fill orbital 1s by making an electron pair and the third enters orbital 2s the one with the next lowest energy. With the fourth electron of beryllium to complete the electron pair, orbital 2s becomes full.

The next electrons go into the 2p-orbitals and there are three of them. There will be no electron-pairs until all have a single electron in them. This situation is reached with nitrogen. Oxygen, fluorine and neon have an electron pair in the s-orbitals and respectively one, two and three electron-pairs in the p-orbitals. Then the second shell is full and the next electron starts a new third shell.

So it continues, in a satisfying and logical way until all the elements are placed in the periodic table. Do not confuse the diagram opposite with the energy levels available in any given atom. Since each element has a unique number of protons and electrons, it also has a unique pattern of energy levels and quantum jumps. That is why elements can be recognised by their spectra.

Valence electrons

If you look at the diagram opposite you will see that the 4s, 5s, 6s, & 7s-orbitals step downwards and are of lower energy than the d & f-orbitals of previous shells. This means that electrons will enter these s-orbitals and start a new shell before the previous shell or shells are full. It is also true that the p-orbitals of one shell always have lower energy than the s-orbitals of the next. A most important consequence which follows from this fact is that the outermost shell never contains more than 8 electrons.

When we talk about the chemical properties of an element, we are really talking about the way that it reacts and combines with other elements. These reactions are determined by electronic structures because when elements bond together to form compounds, they transfer or share electrons. The general name of 'valence' is given to the tendency to form compounds by a change in the electronic structure and so those electrons most involved in reactions with other atoms, those in the outer shell, are called the 'valence electrons'. The outer shell, whichever it may be, is known as the valence shell.

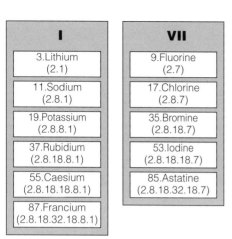

I
3.Lithium (2.1)
11.Sodium (2.8.1)
19.Potassium (2.8.8.1)
37.Rubidium (2.8.18.8.1)
55.Caesium (2.8.18.18.8.1)
87.Francium (2.8.18.32.18.8.1)

VII
9.Fluorine (2.7)
17.Chlorine (2.8.7)
35.Bromine (2.8.18.7)
53.Iodine (2.8.18.18.7)
85.Astatine (2.8.18.32.18.7)

Two chemical groups showing their electronic structures.

VIII
2.Helium (2)
10.Neon (2.8)
18.Argon (2.8.8)
36.Krypton (2.8.18.8)
54.Xenon (2.8.18.18.8)
86.Radon (2.8.18.32.18.8)

Mendeleev and the chemical groups

If you remember, Mendeleev first ordered the known elements by mass and then formed his columns by putting elements which had similar compounds above and below each other. He was not aware that he was arranging them according to the number of electrons in the outer shell, but that is what he was doing. The periodicity that he observed was due to the fact that there can only be either 1, 2, 3, 4, 5, 6, 7 or 8 electrons in the valence shell. He of course missed the '8' because the noble gases had not then been discovered.

Each of the elements in a vertical column of the periodic table has the same number of electrons in its outer shell and they therefore form what is known as a 'chemical group' or a 'family group'. They share many chemical and physical properties. Two typical groups are shown on the left. Mendeleev noticed that hydrogen stood apart in some way and that although he thought that copper should be placed in the first column, it did not seem fully at home there. He was right to be concerned about these two elements and indeed about others and his doubts confirm what a fine scientist he was. He was totally convinced by the truth of his theory, but did not allow this enthusiasm to blind him to its weaknesses and to certain inconsistencies. The modern understanding of the electronic structure of the atom has made it possible to place each element in its proper place. See the latest version of the periodic table on page 142.

This understanding has also shown that although most chemical properties and chemical reactions depend on the number of electrons in the outer shell, the number in any incomplete inner shell also exerts an influence. Of course, although Mendeleev himself did not know about the noble gases or the eighth column, it is clear why their discovery has confirmed rather than upset his theory.

The noble gases

This diagram shows the full electronic structures of the six noble gases. The most significant point about them is that in each case the valence shell is full. In the case of helium the outer shell only requires two electrons to be full but for all the others it requires eight.

A complete shell of electrons has a considerable stability and resistance to interference from other atoms. This means that it plays little role in chemical reactions. Because of their structure the noble gases can scarcely be persuaded to take part in any chemical reactions at all and no compounds of helium, neon or argon have yet been discovered. It is not surprising that they remained unknown and unsuspected for so long.

VIII
29.Copper (2.8.18.1)
47.Silver (2.8.18.18.1)
79.Gold (2.8.18.32.18.1)

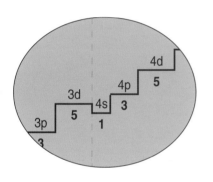

Orbital	Max Electrons	Element	Electronic Structure
4s	2	19. Potassium	2.8.8.1
		20. Calcium	2.8.8.2
3d	10	21. Scandium	2.8.9.2
		22. Titanium	2.8.10.2
		23. Vanadium	2.8.11.2
		24. Chromium	2.8.13.1
		25. Manganese	2.8.13.2
		26. Iron	2.8.14.2
		27. Cobalt	2.8.15.2
		28. Nickel	2.8.16.2
		29. Copper	2.8.18.1
		30. Zinc	2.8.18.2
4p	6	31. Gallium	2.8.18.3
		32. Germanium	2.8.18.4

Copper, silver and gold

These three elements have similar electronic structures and share many properties. All three were known in antiquity and are sometimes found in their metallic form in nature. They have ores from which the metal can easily be extracted and have long been used for coinage and jewellery. They are easy to work but since they are rather soft, they are usually alloyed with other metals to make them more wear-resistant. Copper is mixed with tin to make bronze, silver with copper to make sterling silver and gold with silver. They form a sub-group, which is now numbered 11 but was previously numbered IB.

Although each has one valence electron like sodium and potassium and might be expected also to be very active chemically, their inner shells have the magic numbers of 18 & 32 and they go some way towards the stability of the inert gases. This is especially true of gold which remains untarnished over centuries and has been highly valued by all civilisations as a way of symbolising purity and eternity.

Filling inner shells, the first transition metals

Energy level 4s is the first to step down to a lower level than the previous one and so the fourth shell starts before the third is complete. The first two elements with electrons in orbital 4s are potassium and calcium. After those, the next set of orbitals to fill are the five of 3d, giving exactly 10 elements. They are known as the first transition metals and elements 21-30 are the earliest elements in the periodic table where the filling takes place in an inner shell. As might be expected, they all have many similar chemical properties. However, all these elements are clearly distinguishable from each other and in the modern group numbering system they belong to different groups.

A surprising fact to notice is that both chromium and copper do not have two valence electrons as might be expected, but one. Granted their positions in the table it would be logical for their electronic structures to be (2.8.12.2) and (2.8.17.2). However, this is not what actually happens in practice because the arrangements (2.8.13.1) and (2.8.18.1) each have slightly lower energy.

Mendeleev also noticed that certain groups of adjacent elements also shared many properties. Within this first group of transition metals are the three elements iron, cobalt and nickel which do so. They form what is known as the first triad and are strongly magnetic. All three are found together in meteorites.

Filling inner shells, the rare earths

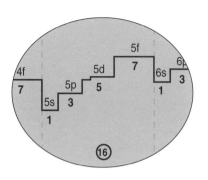

The collective name of these fourteen elements is something of a confusion as they are neither rare nor earths. This mis-naming arose because it was originally thought that their oxides were the elements. It was only later that their true nature was appreciated. All of them are soft, malleable metals and even the least common is as plentiful as iodine.

Notice how the energy levels 5s, 5p and 6s are all lower than 4f. The outer shell of each of these elements contains the 2 electrons in orbitals 6s and the next either 8 or 9 electrons. The filling of the seven 4f-orbitals takes place in the third shell from the outside and this explains why the chemical properties of this group of fourteen elements are so very similar. Where one element occurs, so do most or all of the others and they are very difficult to separate from each other. Energy level 5d is itself split and is at almost the same level as 4f. Element 57, Lanthanum, is often included in the rare earths, although it does not have any electrons in the 4f-orbitals. Indeed, the rare earths are sometimes known as the lanthanides.

The rare earths are not found in many places around the globe, but are concentrated at a few particular sites in Scandinavia, Siberia, Greenland, North America, Brazil and India. The best known site is near Ytterby in Sweden, a place which has given its name to the three elements, ytterbium, erbium and yttrium.

The most common element of the group, cerium, is more plentiful than either tin or lead but, unlike them, relatively few practical uses have been found so far. The best known is to make the 'flints' in lighters, as when combined with iron to give misch-metal, it gives off a spark when struck. It is also used in catalytic converters for motor cars. Some rare earths are ingredients in the exciting new discoveries of high temperature superconductors.

The man-made elements

The fundamental difference between one element and another lies in the number of protons in the nucleus and so to create a new element, protons must be added or taken away. Nuclear research has shown that bombardment with high energy particles can achieve this and a particularly exciting technique has been to add more protons to large nuclei and so produce elements with atomic numbers above 92. At the time of writing, all the elements as far as 109 have been created and named. Whatever the positive charge in the nucleus, the same number of electrons are attracted and they settle into a new configuration with the lowest energy. So far, all the man-made elements have two electrons in the outer shell. Some of these new elements have half-lives measured in thousands or millions of years and will therefore continue to exist on earth for a long time to come.

Max Electrons Orbital		Element	Electronic Structure
5d	2	57. Lanthanum	2.8.18.18.9.2
4f	14	58. Cerium	2.8.18.18.8.2
		59. Praseodymium	2.8.18.21.8.2
		60. Neodymium	2.8.18.22.8.2
		61. Promethium	2.8.18.23.8.2
		62. Samarium	2.8.18.24.8.2
		63. Europium	2.8.18.25.8.2
		64. Gadolinium	2.8.18.25.9.2
		65. Terbium	2.8.18.27.8.2
		66. Dysprosium	2.8.18.28.8.2
		67. Holmium	2.8.18.29.8.2
		68. Erbium	2.8.18.30.8.2
		69. Thulium	2.8.18.31.8.2
		70. Ytterbium	2.8.18.32.8.2
		71. Lutetium	2.8.18.32.9.2

43.Technetium
61. Promethium

93.Neptunium
94.Plutonium
95.Americium
96.Curium
97.Berkelium
98.Californium
99.Einsteinium
100.Fermium
101.Mendelevium
102.Nobelium
103.Lawrencium
104.Rutherfordium
105.Hahnium
106.Seaborgium
107.Nielsbohrium
108.Hassium
109.Meitnerium

As a general rule, as the atomic number increases, so the elements become increasingly unstable. Elements 108 and 109 have half-lives of only a few thousandths of a second and this is not long enough to find out much about them. Only a few atoms have ever been created and each of them has been detected essentially only by the manner in which they disappeared!

The heaviest element to exist naturally on earth is uranium and all the first 92 elements with just two exceptions, technetium and promethium have been found. Neither of these has any stable isotopes and the half-lives of others too short for natural deposits still to exist. Technetium was the first example of a man-made element. It was first created in 1937 by adding a proton to molybdenum. Since its half-life is 4.2 million years, it will now be present on earth for a very long time into the future. The same cannot be said of promethium unless it is continually being remade because its most stable isotope has a half-life of only 17.8 years.

Where did the chemical elements come from?

While some details remain to be resolved, a broad picture of the origin of the chemical elements on earth and elsewhere in the universe has been pieced together by astronomers.

The lightest elements, hydrogen and nearly all helium, were made within the first few minutes after the Big Bang. After about 100,000 years and as the universe cooled, protons combined with electrons to form hydrogen and protons, neutrons and electrons to form helium. Helium then made up 24% of matter and hydrogen 76%. Small amounts of deuterium and lithium were also produced. Then there was a long period, perhaps billions of years, while the galaxies and stars slowly condensed out of the rapidly expanding, but initially uniform gas generated by the Big Bang. When the local density became high enough to support nuclear reactions, the stars ignited. Within those stars, some additional helium was created from hydrogen, but added only a small fraction to what already existed. All the other elements were made by nuclear reactions in the interior of stars.

As the hydrogen was used up, these stars reached the end of their lifetimes and spectacular supernovae explosions threw huge quantities of heavy elements, particularly iron, out into space. This material then mixed with the primeval hydrogen and helium and condensed into a new generation of stars. The process then repeated but this time heavier elements existed and planets such as earth could be formed. Possibly more than 92 elements but certainly 90 were present in the new born earth. It is fascinating to realise that all the elements which now make up our bodies, excepting hydrogen have been made in earlier stars.

The search for the chemical elements ends on earth and within ourselves!

The Periodic Table
Showing the New and Traditional Chemical Groups

Elements where electrons are being added to an outer shell

	New Groups								
	1	**2**		**13**	**14**	**15**	**16**	**17**	**18**

1s — 1 Hydrogen

1s — 1 Hydrogen | 2 Helium

2s	3 Lithium	4 Beryllium	2p	5 Boron	6 Carbon	7 Nitrogen	8 Oxygen	9 Fluorine	10 Neon
3s	11 Sodium	12 Magnesium	3p	13 Aluminium	14 Silicon	15 Phosphorus	16 Sulphur	17 Chlorine	18 Argon
4s	19 Potassium	20 Calcium	3d [21-30] 4p	31 Gallium	32 Germanium	33 Arsenic	34 Selenium	35 Bromine	36 Krypton
5s	37 Rubidium	38 Strontium	4d [39-48] 5p	49 Indium	50 Tin	51 Antimony	52 Tellurium	53 Iodine	54 Xenon
6s	55 Caesium	56 Barium	4f [57-70] 5d [71-80] 6p	81 Thallium	82 Lead	83 Bismuth	84 Polonium	85 Astatine	86 Radon
7s	87 Francium	88 Radium	5f [89-102] 6d [103-]						

Traditional Groups: **I** **II** ... **III** **IV** **V** **VI** **VII** **VIII**

4f [57-70]

| 57 Lanthanum | 58 Cerium | 59 Praseodymium | 60 Neodymium | 61 Promethium | 62 Samarium | 63 Europium | 64 Gadolinium | 65 Terbium | 66 Dysprosium | 67 Holmium | 68 Erbium | 69 Thulium | 70 Ytterbium |

Lanthanides (Rare Earths)

5f [89-102]

| 89 Actinium | 90 Thorium | 91 Protactinium | 92 Uranium | 93 Neptunium | 94 Plutonium | 95 Americium | 96 Curium | 97 Berkelium | 98 Californium | 99 Einsteinium | 100 Fermium | 101 Mendelevium | 102 Nobelium |

Actinides

'Transitional' elements where electrons are being added to an inner shell

	3	**4**	**5**	**6**	**7**	**8**	**9**	**10**	**11**	**12**
3d	21 Scandium	22 Titanium	23 Vanadium	24 Chromium	25 Manganese	26 Iron	27 Cobalt	28 Nickel	29 Copper	30 Zinc
4d	39 Yttrium	40 Zirconium	41 Niobium	42 Molybdenum	43 Technetium	44 Ruthenium	45 Rhodium	46 Palladium	47 Silver	48 Cadmium
4f [57-70] 5d	71 Lutetium	72 Hafnium	73 Tantalum	74 Tungsten	75 Rhenium	76 Osmium	77 Iridium	78 Platinum	79 Gold	80 Mercury
5f [89-102] 6d	103 Lawrencium	104 Rutherfordium	105 Hahnium	106 Seaborgium	107 Nielsbohrium	108 Hassium	109 Meitnerium		IB	IIB
	IIIB	**IVB**	**VB**	**VIB**	**VIIB**		**VIIIB**			

The Elements
Their Symbols, Atomic Numbers and Relative Atomic Masses

Name	Symbol	Atomic Number	Relative Atomic Mass
Actinium	Ac	89	227.0
Aluminium	Al	13	27.0
Americium	Am	95	(243)
Antimony	Sb	51	121.8
Argon	Ar	18	39.9
Arsenic	As	33	74.9
Astatine	At	85	(210)
Barium	Ba	56	137.3
Berkelium	Bk	97	(247)
Beryllium	Be	4	9.0
Bismuth	Bi	83	209.0
Boron	B	5	10.8
Bromine	Br	35	79.9
Cadmium	Cd	48	112.4
Caesium	Cs	55	132.9
Calcium	Ca	20	40.1
Californium	Cf	98	(251)
Carbon	C	6	12.0
Cerium	Ce	58	140.1
Chlorine	Cl	17	35.5
Chromium	Cr	24	52.0
Cobalt	Co	27	58.9
Copper	Cu	29	63.5
Curium	Cm	96	(247)
Dysprosium	Dy	66	162.5
Einsteinium	Es	99	(252)
Erbium	Er	68	167.3
Europium	Eu	63	152.0
Fermium	Fm	100	(257)
Fluorine	F	9	19.0
Francium	Fr	87	(223)
Gadolinium	Gd	64	157.3
Gallium	Ga	31	69.7
Germanium	Ge	32	72.6
Gold	Au	79	197.0
Hafnium	Hf	72	178.5
Hahnium	Ha	105	(262)
Hassium	Hs	108	(265)
Helium	He	2	4.0
Holmium	Ho	67	164.9
Hydrogen	H	1	1.0
Indium	In	49	114.8
Iodine	I	53	126.9
Iridium	Ir	77	192.2
Iron	Fe	26	55.8
Krypton	Kr	36	83.8
Lanthanum	La	57	138.9
Lawrencium	Lr	103	(260)
Lead	Pb	82	207.2
Lithium	Li	3	6.9
Lutetium	Lu	71	175.0
Magnesium	Mg	12	24.3
Manganese	Mn	25	54.9
Meitnerium	Mt	109	(266)
Mendelevium	Md	101	(258)
Mercury	Hg	80	200.6
Molybdenum	Mo	42	95.9
Neodymium	Nd	60	144.2
Neon	Ne	10	20.2
Neptunium	Np	93	237.0
Nickel	Ni	28	58.7
Nielsbohrium	Ns	107	(262)
Niobium	Nb	41	92.9
Nitrogen	N	7	14.0
Nobelium	No	102	(259)
Osmium	Os	76	190.2
Oxygen	O	8	16.0
Palladium	Pd	46	106.4
Phosphorus	P	15	31.0
Platinum	Pt	78	195.1
Plutonium	Pu	94	(244)
Polonium	Po	84	(209)
Potassium	K	19	39.1
Praseodymium	Pr	59	140.9
Promethium	Pm	61	(145)
Protactinium	Pa	91	231.0
Radium	Ra	88	(226)
Radon	Rn	86	(222)
Rhenium	Re	75	186.2
Rhodium	Rh	45	102.9
Rubidium	Rb	37	85.5
Ruthenium	Ru	44	101.1
Rutherfordium	Rf	104	(261)
Samarium	Sm	62	150.4
Scandium	Sc	21	45.0
Seaborgium	Sg	106	(263)
Selenium	Se	34	79.0
Silicon	Si	14	28.1
Silver	Ag	47	107.9
Sodium	Na	11	23.0
Strontium	Sr	38	87.6
Sulphur	S	16	32.1
Tantalum	Ta	73	180.9
Technetium	Tc	43	(98.0)
Tellurium	Te	52	127.6
Terbium	Tb	65	158.9
Thallium	Tl	81	204.4
Thorium	Th	90	232.0
Thulium	Tm	69	168.9
Tin	Sn	50	118.7
Titanium	Ti	22	47.9
Tungsten	W	74	183.9
Uranium	U	92	238.0
Vanadium	V	23	50.9
Xenon	Xe	54	131.3
Ytterbium	Yb	70	173.0
Yttrium	Y	39	88.9
Zinc	Zn	30	65.4
Zirconium	Zr	40	91.2

Index